Sand dunes, Death Valley, with Grapevine Mountains in background.

OUR CHANGING EARTH

THROUGH THE AGES

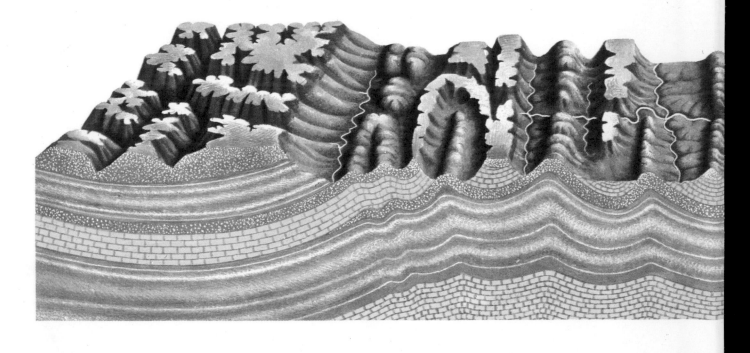

THE STORY OF
GEOLOGY

by Jerome Wyckoff

Illustrated with Photographs
and with Paintings by
William Sayles, Harry McNaught, and Raymond Perlman

GOLDEN PRESS ⬚ NEW YORK

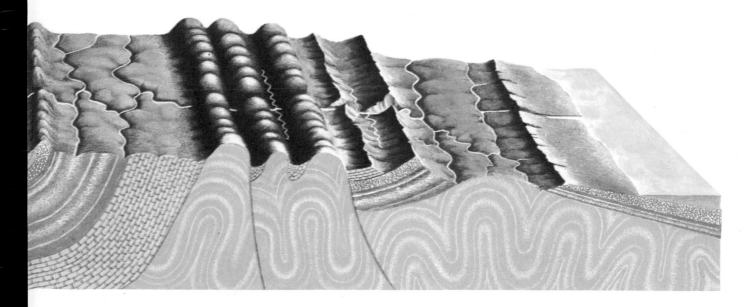

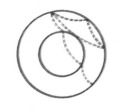

Library of Congress Catalog Card Number: 60-14878

CONTENTS

ACKNOWLEDGMENTS

The author and the publishers are indebted to Dr. Brian Mason, Curator of Physical Geology and Mineralogy, American Museum of Natural History, and to Dr. George Gaylord Simpson, Museum of Comparative Zoölogy, Harvard University, for professional advice generously given in regard to the text and the illustrations. Thanks are due also to the Photo Library, U. S. Geological Survey, Denver, and the American Geographical Society, New York, for aid in the search for photographic material.

The maps on pp. 72-73 are adapted (with changes) by permission from *Geology of the Great Lakes* by Jack L. Hough, Univ. of Illinois Press, Urbana, Ill., 1958. The maps on p. 115 were drawn from information contained in similar maps in *Historical Geology* by Carl O. Dunbar, John Wiley & Sons, New York, 1960. *The Global Atlas* (Golden Press, New York, 1958) is the source of the map on p. 118. Information for the diagram on p. 137 was provided by Esso. The maps on pp. 158-163 were prepared on the basis of material provided by Lamont Geological Observatory, by permission of Bruce C. Heezen.

The paintings by Raymond Perlman are from *Rocks and Minerals* by Zim and Shaffer, copyright 1957 by Golden Press, New York.

ART CREDITS

HARRY MCNAUGHT: cover, 4-5, 7-9, 12, 16, 18t, 22, 26-27, 32-33, 41b, 42b, 47b, 54b, 59t, 60, 66-67, 67t, 74, 75b, 84b, 104t, 111b, 112t, 116-117b, 118b, 152, 162-163t, 168-169t

RAYMOND PERLMAN: 35t, 36t, 104b, 106b, 109, 111t, 140t, 140-141b, 144-145, 146, 150, 151t

WILLIAM SAYLES: 63b, 68b, 71, 72-73b, 80, 82t, 87, 90-91b, 94-95, 98t, 103, 110, 113t, 115, 121b, 123, 126, 129, 133, 134t, 136, 137, 142, 149, 151b, 153b, 155, 156-157b, 158, 160t, 161, 165, 172-173, 174

PHOTOGRAPH CREDITS

Elvin Abeles: 83t, 106tr
Adprint, Ltd., London: 120
Aerofilms, Ltd.: 61b
American Geographical Society: 37b, 62b
American Museum of Natural History: 166, 168b, 170b
ANACONDA: 148
Andre de Lavarre—Philip D. Gendreau: 28t
Annan Photo Features: 75t
Ray Atkeson: 45b, 73t, 155
Robert Bagby—FPG: 78-79
     Bird: 169b
Jack Breed—FPG: 47
Horace Bristol—FPG: 37t
British Information Service: 21t
B. A. Butt—Philip D. Gendreau: 63t
Barnum Brown: 15, 18b, 51t, 171
Camera Clix: 59b
Canadian National Travel Bureau: 97b, 108
State of Colorado: 56t, 57, 122, 128
Leon Deller—Monkmeyer: 162
Ed Ellinger—Shostal: back endpapers
Bob Ellis—FPG: 114
Georgia Engelhard—Monkmeyer: 96m
Carlos Elmer: 10-11, 52t, 130
William O. Field—American Geographical Society: 101b
Dave Forbert—Shostal: 131t
Freeport Sulphur Co.—FLO: 86-87
Philip D. Gendreau: 32, 81t
State of Georgia Dept. of Commerce: 143
Samuel P. Haberman: 46t, 46b
Fritz Henle—Monkmeyer: 131b
Idaho Dept. of Commerce: 30-31
Italian State Tourist Office: 39
Kaare Haug: 156-157
Russ Kinne: 70, 83b
Lamont Geological Observatory: 163
Hubert Lowman: 53b
Laurence Lowry—Rapho Guillaumette: 62t, 74t
Luray Caverns: 64
Steve McCutcheon: 17, 96t

William Maher: 56b
David Muench: 28-29
Joseph Muench: 20, 30-31, 36b, 43, 48-49, 50t, 55t, 61t, 69b, 84t, 85t, 94, 95, 97t, 116t, 124-125, 127, front endpapers
National Park Service: 42t, 54t, 90t, 99, 107t
Oregon State Highway Dept.: 34b, 89t
New York Public Library: 132, 154, 159
Ruth Pieroth: 35b, 53t, 81b, 91t, 121b
Rutherford Platt: 96b
Paul Popper, Ltd.—Annan Photo Features: 13
F. H. Pough—American Museum of Natural History: 38t
     Rice: 134b
Rock of Ages Corp., Barre, Vt.: 138
Royal Canadian Air Force: 119
Francis P. Shepard: 160
Bernard G. Silberstein—Monkmeyer: 34t
Sinclair Oil Corp.: 113br
Dick Smith: 98b
Soil Conservation Comm., U. S. Dept. of Agriculture: 52b, 86t
South Dakota Dept. of Highways, Publicity Dept.: 50b, 102
Bob and Ira Spring: 19, 44, 72t, 167
Werner Stoy—FPG: 164
Bob Taylor—FPG: 77
Univ. of New South Wales: 38b, 112b
UPI: 55b, 135
U. S. Forest Service, Dept. of Agriculture: 100t
U. S. Geological Survey: 109b
U. S. Navy—American Geographical Society: 40, 41, 92-93
Utah Tourist and Publicity Agency: 175
Harold Wanless: 21b, 23t, 23b, 51b, 68t, 105b, 116b, 118t
Ward's Natural Science Establishment: 110b, 113bl, 139, 170t
Stephen Warner—Shostal: 76
George Wolfson: 14
Jerome Wyckoff: 45t, 85b, 101t, 105t, 107b, 106tl, 117t, 1401, 141t
Jack Zehrt—FPG: 88

FOREWORD

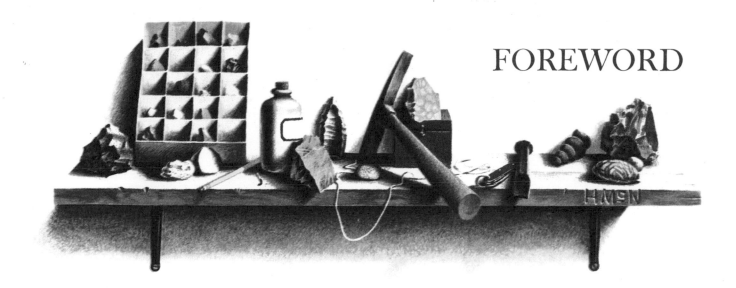

EARTH as we see it today is one frame of a moving picture that has been running for billions of years, and will run for billions of years more. Wherever we are, all around us, the ages-long story of erosion, of lands rising and falling, of volcanoes erupting and glaciers forming, of rocks and minerals being created, is in the making. Within one's own life span, the changes may seem infinitesimally small, but in geology a thousand years are as a day.

As an outdoor-minded people, we are becoming more aware of geological features around us. We travel thousands of miles to see the Grand Canyon and Yosemite, Niagara Falls and the Great Lakes, the Appalachian Mountains and the volcanoes of Mexico, the coasts of Cape Cod and Oregon. More and more of us become "rock hounds" and fossil hunters. Geology, the study of Earth's crust, becomes a fascinating story that he who travels can learn to read.

This is a book for people who like the feel of Earth underfoot, who want to know the meanings of landscapes and seascapes. But also it is a book that shows how the phenomena of Earth's crust influence our whole way of life. The bricks and cement for our houses and highways, the metals for our automobiles and appliances, the coal for our fuels and plastics, even the soil for our crops—all these are from the planet's crust. The stages of human history, from the Stone Age through the Copper and Bronze, to the Iron Age and now the Atomic Era, reflect man's increasing knowledge and use of mineral resources.

We are, every one of us, intimate parts of the world of the geologist.

This book ventures across the borders of such sciences as meteorology, the study of weather and climate; geophysics, which concentrates on Earth's interior; and paleontology, which deals with life of the past. But it is essentially the story of geology. I welcome this effort to tell it as living, exciting knowledge.

BRIAN MASON

Curator of Physical Geology and Mineralogy
American Museum of Natural History

Changing Earth

WHEN we look at a mountain or a desert, a valley or a sea, it seems that they must always have been as they are now. Man can cut down a forest or blast a small hill away, but who can build a mountain or set the boundaries of an ocean? No wonder people use such expressions as "the everlasting hills" and "the eternal sea."

Actually, Earth is constantly being transformed. The process has been going on for several billion years and will go on for billions of years more.

Some of the changes on this planet are sudden and exciting. When a volcano blows its top, a great river floods over its banks, or an earthquake shakes the land—we take notice. But mostly the changes are slow. Five or ten thousand years to make a desert... a hundred thousand years to cut a small valley... ten million years to build a mountain range. That is how Earth uses time.

Think of some of the ways in which Earth is, at this very moment, changing:

All the mountains of the world are being destroyed. Frost, gravity, running water—such forces are wearing them down, grain by grain. Some day the highest mountains will be no more.

Sea bottoms in some regions are rising. Ages from now they will be peaks among the clouds. The rate of rising may be only an inch per year, but Earth has time.

There are places where the sea is creeping in over the land. Some day in those places fish and crabs will swim where cities were.

As recently as 10,000 years ago, great ice sheets covered most of North America and northern Europe. The ice has now melted back all the way to Greenland and other arctic regions. But the climate could get warmer still. In another 10,000 years all Greenland could be as warm as Florida today.

Book of Earth—*Rock layers of Grand Canyon record a billion years of Earth history. Colorado River has taken two million years to cut mile-deep gorge. View here is from Toroweap Point.*

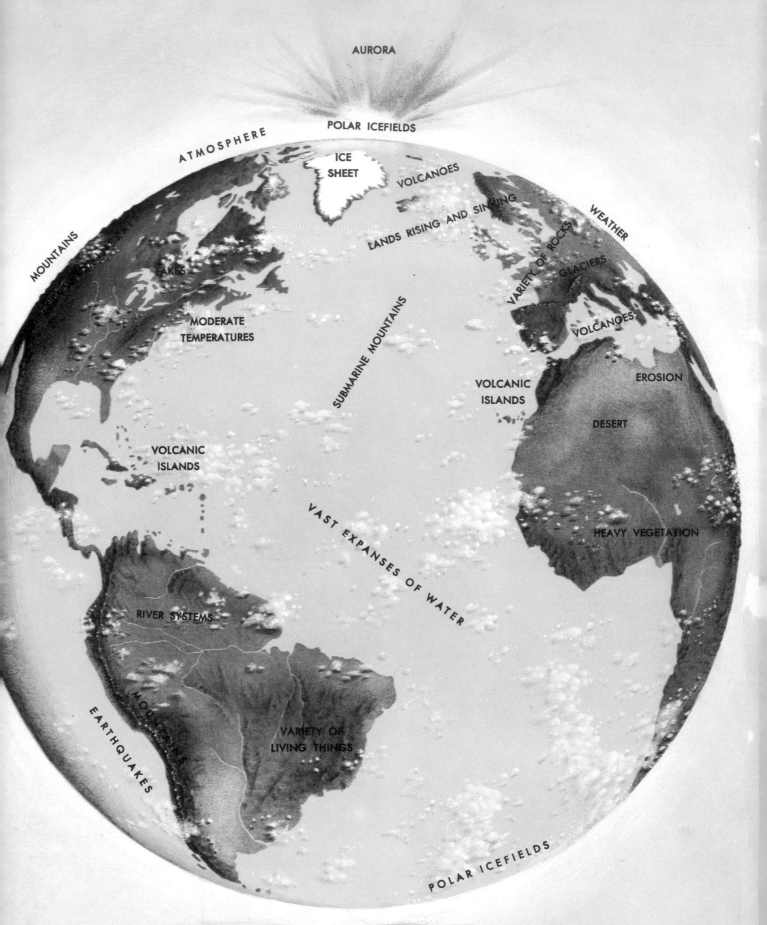

Geologist's view of Earth—*Our planet, with abundant atmosphere, varied landscapes, plentiful water, moderate temperatures, is unique in Solar System.*

Does anyone suppose there can be only one Grand Canyon in Earth's history? There have been greater ones, and there will be more. Somewhere on the globe, rivers have already begun cutting these canyons.

As hills wear down, their remains—sand, clay, stones—are washed and blown down into valleys, across the land, even out to sea. Grain by grain, layer by layer, this old rock material is piling up. Suppose the average rate of accumulation in the world's great basins is a foot every thousand years. Even so, these sediments, gradually turning to hard rock again, will in some regions become miles thick.

In layers of sedimentary rock exposed around us, fossils are found—remains or imprints of animals and plants of prehistoric times. The remains of plants and animals of our times, too, are drifting down into the mud and ooze, to become fossils for the next billion years.

The inland seas of our time—the Great Lakes, the Caspian Sea, and the others—have been where they are for thousands of years. But that is only a second on the geological clock. A few more seconds and the sparkling waters will be gone.

Deep in Earth, in the domain of terrific heat and pressures, other forces are busy. Limestones are being changed into marble, clay into mica, masses of dead plants into coal. Earth's dark interior everywhere is a laboratory, with a work day millions of years long.

Here and there, Earth's crust bends or bulges a little, and breaks. White-hot material from the depths surges upward through cracks. Some bursts out through volcanoes; some flows out on ocean floors; some forces its way between underground strata of rock. Thus the planet's crust is being replenished, and new lands built.

As Earth circles the Sun, the axis around which it spins gradually changes. In the past, our north and south poles probably have been thousands of miles from where they are today. The poles may still be wandering, and no one knows where they will be a million years hence.

A hundred thousand years from now, the place where you are reading these words may be under a mile of ice—or it may be in a warm swamp like the Florida Everglades. In a million years it may be a sea bottom, half a mile below the waves. Fifty million years from today, it may be a land of snow-capped mountains.

Such are the ways of changing Earth.

OUR REMARKABLE PLANET

Among all the planets of the solar system, Earth is very likely the most diversified, the most changeable, the most picturesque.

Some other members of the Sun's family have atmospheres and, therefore, weather. None can match all the varied displays seen on Earth—blue skies patched with clouds, flaming sunrises and sunsets, rainbows and blizzards, sleet storms and April showers.

No other planet, apparently, offers majestic mountain ranges, sprawling glaciers, and rushing rivers. Mars has deserts and dust storms to match the Sahara's, but only Earth shows sunlit lakes and landscapes of living green. One can doubt that cloud-hidden Venus—our nearest cousin—has water-carved Grand Canyons and badlands. Mercury could have volcanoes, and the great red spot in Jupiter's banded clouds may be a region of heat; but with such exceptions, volcanoes and geysers and hot springs are Earth's alone.

Only on Earth—*Picturesque, fertile, well-watered landscapes, like this one near Calstock, England, do not exist on any other planet in Solar System.*

Once a rolling prairie?—*Grand Tetons of Wyoming, here mirrored in Jackson Lake, have been carved by glaciers and running water out of huge block raised out of Earth's crust millions of years ago.*

The cutting of valleys by rivers, the tunneling of the crust by ground water, the phenomena of springs and swamps—these probably will never be seen in the solar system except on our world. The mineral wealth here, which depends upon weather as well as the original rocks, is probably unique.

It is almost certain (the doubt lies again in Venus) that only Earth possesses plentiful supplies of liquid water—liquid thanks to our moderate temperatures. It is liquid water that supports all living things; and, more than any other agent, it is water and ice that, through erosion, keep the planet's surface constantly changing.

Earth, as the only planet supporting a large variety of living things, surely is unmatched as a museum and graveyard for the life of the past. On no other planet, at least within this solar system, are there men to read the history in the rocks, and to contemplate vanished worlds.

THE OCEAN OF AIR

First among the forces at work upon our changing Earth is the atmosphere. Powered mostly by the Sun's heat, and working with the planet's abundant supply of water, the air keeps the grand processes of erosion going. Thanks to the atmosphere, lands high and low are shaped by water, ice, and wind. And, as we shall see later in this book, the shaping of the lands in turn has many remarkable and unexpected results.

This wide-working atmosphere is a deep ocean. At its bottom live people, animals, and plants much as fish, oysters, and seaweeds live in the sea. Wherever we go, on land or in the air, we are in the atmosphere. We think no more about it than a fish thinks about swimming.

Air is made up of molecules and atoms of gas, and of free electrons—all very tiny particles of matter too small to see even in a microscope.

14

These particles have spaces between them. Near Earth's surface, the particles are crowded together under the weight of all the air above them. But as one moves higher off the ground, the spaces get wider. Beyond 250 miles, the spaces are so wide that there is practically no air at all. Here the air offers only the tiniest resistance to satellites as they circle our planet, month after month.

The weight of the atmosphere at sea level is more than 14 pounds on every square inch of area. That is about one ton per square foot. On mountain heights, the pressure is much lighter—about 5½ pounds, for example, on Mount Everest. At least three fourths of all the atmosphere is packed into the part that is within ten miles of the ground.

At heights of fifty to one hundred miles, the air is so thin that we could scarcely feel a wind blowing on our faces at hundreds of miles per hour. Yet that thin air blocks out most of the cosmic rays from outer space—deadly radiation like that from atomic bombs. If all these rays reached Earth's surface, neither man nor, perhaps, any other form of life could exist there.

These upper levels of air also act as shields against meteors. Showers of these bits of stone and metal race through our solar system at speeds up to sixty miles per second, and Earth plows through them like an automobile through rain. Fortunately, most meteors heat up from friction with the atmosphere and turn to vapor or dust by the time they get down to the fifty-mile-high level. A few are too big to vaporize entirely, and pieces reach the earth as "meteorites." Once every thousand years or so, a giant meteor gets through the atmosphere and blasts a crater hundreds of feet wide in the ground. Possibly Earth formed from the aggregation, or lumping together, of meteoritic material billions of years ago, when the solar system was young.

THE EVER-MOVING ATMOSPHERE

The blanket of gases around Earth is constantly being disturbed. Light rays from the Sun keep shooting down into it, and many reach the

Cutting power of water—*Air view of Painted Desert, Arizona, shows intricate gullying which is destroying landscape. In such arid regions, lack of vegetation makes erosion more apparent than elsewhere.*

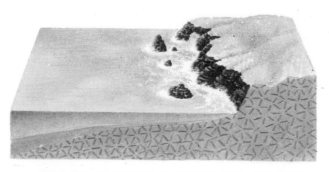

EROSION OF COASTS BY WAVES AND CURRENTS

CARVING OF LANDSCAPES BY RUNNING WATER

SHAPING OF LANDS BY ICE

UNDERGROUND TUNNELING BY GROUND WATER

DEPOSIT OF DEBRIS IN BASINS

ground. Striking the air and dust particles, and the ground itself, these rays produce heat, just as sunlight pouring into a greenhouse makes heat there. This heat starts the tiny particles of air moving faster, and they get farther apart. But air with particles farther apart is lighter than air with particles close together. The warmer, lighter air tends to rise above the colder, heavier air, and so air currents and winds are started.

The atmosphere is disturbed also by the Moon's gravity. Just as the pull of the Moon causes tides in the ocean, it causes tides in the air. These tides may have much to do with our weather.

Still another disturber of the air is our planet's rotation. The atmosphere tends to remain stationary as the solid ball of Earth rotates within it. But the friction of the air against the ground does cause some movement of the lower part of the atmosphere, and this affects wind directions.

THE TRAVELS OF WATER

As air moves over the sea and land, it picks up moisture in the form of very tiny particles called water vapor. These tiny particles float between the particles of air. The warmer the air is, the wider the spaces between its particles are and the more water particles it can pick up.

Suppose a warm, dry wind from the land blows over the sea. It picks up billions of water particles. Then this air moves over cooler land or cooler waters. The air becomes chilled and can no longer hold so much water.

In the process called condensation, some of this water changes into small, visible drops, which often form around particles of dust. Large, dense groups of these droplets are seen by us as clouds, and from these rain or snow may fall. Some of this fallen water sinks underground. Some is captured by the roots of plants, a little is used by animals and people, and much is evaporated into the air again. But about a fourth of it, by way of rivers, drains back to the sea.

River waters moving downward through the land, pulled by gravity, carry sand, clay, and pebbles. These work in the river channels like scrapers. With help from frost and other agents of erosion, the rivers keep deepening and widening their channels to make valleys.

River of ice—*Ruth Glacier on Mt. McKinley, Alaska, is reminder of ages past during which great ice sheets covered lands now inhabited by man.*

Water freezing in cracks among rocks expands, wedging the rocks apart, loosening them so that gravity can pull them down to lower levels. Water joins gases in the air to eat away the surfaces of rock and soil.

Water moving underground dissolves certain kinds of rock and makes hidden tunnels and caverns. Water in the form of glaciers, the packed snows and ice of a thousand winters, keeps grinding down the mountainsides and cutting the mountain valleys deeper.

Finally, water collects the debris and, with some help from the wind, piles it up on the lowlands and along the seashores where the rivers end.

A SEA WITH ISLANDS

Earth seen from a space ship would look like a sphere of water, spotted with a few islands. No less than 70 per cent of the planet's surface is covered by oceans, lakes, and rivers.

The ocean contains something like 330 million cubic miles of water. Yet if the whole solid portion of Earth were a perfect sphere, sea water would cover it to a depth of only a mile and a half. To reach Earth's core, one would have to go about 3,966 miles further, through rock. The water film represented by the seas can be compared to a film a hundredth of an inch thick over a geographic globe 35 inches in diameter.

There is always, of course, "borrowed" water on and in the land. Perhaps four million cubic miles of water is locked up in mountain glaciers and in ice near the north and south poles. The ice cap over the interior of Greenland is something like 9,000 feet thick. If all the ice in the world melted suddenly, and all the waters flowed into the sea, the level of the sea would rise perhaps 250 feet, and every important seaport of the world—New York, London, and the rest—would be drowned out.

17

BASALT   OCEAN   OCEAN   BASALT

CONTINENT (granite)   CONTINENT (granite)

Crust of Earth—*Cross section illustrates relationship of oceans, continental masses (mainly granite), and underlying rock (mainly basalt). Vertical scale is exaggerated to show details more clearly.*

THE UNDERSEA WORLD

The sea is in unending motion. Currents are caused by Earth's rotation, by river waters pouring into the sea, by differences in temperatures or salt content of the water, and by winds. The Moon's pull keeps great bulges of water—we call them the tides—moving around the planet.

The sea not only provides the atmosphere with water for its work on the land, but also works upon the land directly. Ocean waves and currents are constantly chewing away at the edges of the continents everywhere. Ocean currents also help to shape the ocean bottoms.

Down from the edges of the continents run sloping, sea-covered shelves. As Earth's crust

Earth is a graveyard—*Paleontologist, exploring rich dinosaur fossil bed in Montana badlands, finds clues to vanished world of a hundred million years ago.*

heaves up and down through the millennia, these shelves become dry land, sea bottom, and dry land, over and over again. Even the interiors of the continents are sometimes invaded for a time by ocean waters.

In the dark green depths and the black abysses are vast plains covered with the ooze of millions of years, mixed with rusted bits of countless meteorites that have fallen on the planet through the ages. Running down the middle of the Atlantic, and curving along the shores of the Western Pacific, are undersea mountain ranges. The peaks of some rise barely above the waves to form islands, as in the Lesser Antilles in the Caribbean Sea, and the volcanic islands of the Southwest Pacific. Trenches with bottoms four to seven miles below sea level split the bottoms near these underwater ranges. These are centers of earthquake activity, and near some of them are chains of submarine volcanoes.

In this salty green world, crossed by currents like lazy winds, communities of plants and animals are as varied and as busy as anywhere on land. They too depend on oxygen and carbon dioxide, but it is brought to them by the water, along with needed minerals washed in from the shore. Some of these multitudes of living things, such as the corals and foraminifers, are the builders of reefs, islands, and vast bottom deposits of limestone. Even these tiny organisms have a part in changing the face of the planet.

THE EARTH'S CRUST

The outermost layer, or shell, of Earth is its rocky crust. Wherever we may be—in forest, desert, city, swamp, or ocean—below us lies this rocky crust. This is the bedrock, with patches of broken stone, soil, and water lying on it here and there. Bedrock is the solid stone we see exposed in hillsides, road cuts, and quarries. It is always somewhat cracked. It may have the form of layers, blocks, sheets, columns, or domes, and may be of just about any color or mixture of colors.

Bedrock masses are frequently folded, broken, or tilted. Great blocks and folds have risen to form mountains, and some blocks have sunk to form lowlands. The best places to see bedrocks are in canyons and gorges cut through the rocks by rivers during thousands or millions of years.

The bedrocks are made up of minerals—hundreds of kinds—that have formed from the basic elements of nature. For example, most sandstone is made of quartz grains, and quartz is made of the elements silicon and oxygen. Most limestone consists of the mineral calcium carbonate, which is made of calcium, oxygen, and carbon.

ROCKS AND SOILS

Bedrocks are essentially of three types. First are the igneous rocks—those that were once molten. Cooled volcanic lavas and granites are examples. Next are the sedimentary rocks: those that formed from crumbled rock material, remains of living things, and minerals precipitated from water. Examples of these are sandstone, shale, limestone, and salt. Finally, there are the metamorphic rocks, which are igneous or sedimentary rocks changed by heat, by pressure, or by liquids or gases percolating through them. Marble, gneiss, and schist are rocks of this sort.

Earth's crust can be imagined as a shell of igneous rocks mostly covered with layers of sedimentary and metamorphic rocks. The surfaces of the continents are mostly sedimentary formations,

Ever-working sea—*World's seashores through the ages are being cut back by waves and currents. Upthrusting forces in Earth's crust have kept continents above water. Scene is at Ecola State Park, Oregon.*

with igneous rocks beneath. Here and there, molten matter has pushed up through other formations, changing them chemically and leaving in them masses of lava that cool in various forms. Igneous rocks probably form the crust under the sediments on the ocean bottoms, too.

The bedrocks are not to be considered as things created once for all time. The conditions that made the rocks we see today still exist, and are making the rocks of tomorrow. Molten material is making new igneous rocks. Sedimentary rocks are being created wherever sediments, such as sand and clay, are packed down by the weight of material above and are cemented by mineral-bearing waters percolating through them. Both igneous and sedimentary rocks are now, as in the past, being converted into metamorphic rock. And all the processes that are producing these three types of rocks are, in so doing, producing new supplies of minerals for Earth's unique stock. It is a pity that despite the vast range and tremendous powers involved in geological events, useful minerals are not being created as fast as man is using them up.

The soils of Earth form only thin layers here and there over the bedrocks. They consist of rock that has been changed chemically, then crumbled into tiny particles, and mixed with decaying remains of plants and animals.

In the broad span of geologic history, soil is just a transition between rock that has been destroyed by erosion and the new rock that will be formed in time from the debris. Certain igneous rocks erode into sands, which may become sandstones, and clays, which may then harden to form shales. Even the black muck of swamps, which has

Rocks formed from sediments—*Majestic sandstone masses, on South Desert in southeast Utah, are remains of ancient landscape formed by hardened sediments. Region was uplifted but is being destroyed by wind and running water. Henry Mountains, in background, are ancient lava formations called laccoliths, exposed by erosion.*

Rocks made in fire—*Large areas of world are covered with rock squeezed up molten from depths. Giants' Causeway, Northern Ireland, is an old lava flow which, as it cooled, cracked to form basalt columns.*

little rock debris in it, may end up as coal or a coaly shale. Although utterly necessary to the existence of living things, soils are, geologically speaking, just rock dust.

RESTLESS ROCK

Mostly, Earth's crust seems quiet, but forces are ever at work on it and within it.

By erosion of the lands, billions of tons of rock waste are carried by wind, running water, and gravity down into low areas. There the rock waste may pile up to such thickness that its weight causes slow sinking of the crust beneath.

Other strains are put on the crust by the gravitational pull of the Moon as it makes its month-long tour around our planet.

Still more strains are due to heat produced in the crust by radioactive materials and chemical processes. This heat may cause pressures that make rock swell, crack, and shift, and thus make the crust rise and sink. Molten rock may come up

through the cracks to form volcanoes, just as air bursts through an auto tube at a weak spot.

Crustal movements are the creators of our mountains. Some mountains rise up as blocks, as a result of up-and-down shifts of crustal sections. Others rise as folds, produced by thrusting forces in the crust as wrinkles are produced in a strip of cloth when it is pushed from the ends.

"Changed" rock—*Gneiss is metamorphic—changed by heat and pressure. Often it is banded, as here.*

21

Crustal movements are usually so minute, so unspectacular, that we are not aware even of mountain ranges rising beneath our feet. But there are exceptions. Stress in the crust here and there causes sudden fractures, and these mean earthquakes. "Earthquake regions" are those in which stresses in the crust are not in balance and readjustments are actively going on.

The end results of even slight and slow movements are the rising and sinking of whole crustal sections. Here, a sea bottom is elevated to become dry land. There, an area of dry land sinks, and the sea creeps in to cover it. Possibly the continents themselves are shifting their positions in response to the forces working below.

How thick Earth's crust may be is a question for argument among scientists. The crust is only two to eight miles thick beneath the trenches in the ocean bottoms, but perhaps forty miles thick beneath some of the lofty mountain ranges on the continents. The deepest mines—the gold mines in South Africa—go down less than two miles, and the deepest oil wells less than five. The center of the planet is nearly 4,000 miles beyond.

The deeper rocks are, the greater is the weight upon them. Ten miles down, the pressure is about 4,600 tons per square foot. That could be compared to the weight of sixteen tons—the weight of six average automobiles—on a single dime.

Inside Earth—*Cutaway view of planet shows comparatively thin crust, thick mantle, and inner and outer cores. Structure is not positively known but is inferred from analysis of seismic waves (see page 137).*

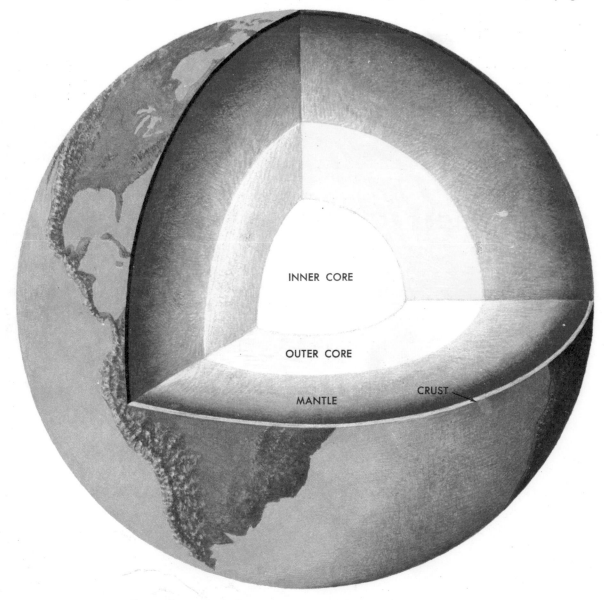

INNER CORE

OUTER CORE

MANTLE

CRUST

Beneath the crust is the mantle, a shell of very heavy rock around 1,800 miles thick. This is truly a place of terrific heat and pressures. Perhaps it is the reservoir of molten matter that feeds volcanoes. Here the temperatures may be around 5,000 degrees above zero Fahrenheit, and the pressure over a million times the pressure of our atmosphere at sea level. That would be equal to about 40,000 tons on the dime.

The mantle rocks are hard—as anything would be under such awful weight. Yet the pressure is so powerful that when there is a disturbance in the mantle, the rock yields. It will bend, twist, or even flow like bread dough. The mantle, seismologists believe, is where the severest of the world's earthquakes originate.

Under the mantle is a region called the outer core. This may consist of nickel and iron, in liquid form because of the enormous heat there. This outer core, perhaps 1,300 miles thick, surrounds the inner core, or "heart" of the planet. The inner core is believed to be a ball of iron and nickel about 1,600 miles in diameter. The ball may be so squeezed that it has shrunk, taking up less space than it would above ground. The pressure on it may be four million times the pressure of the atmosphere at sea level.

In the mantle and the core, geophysicists look for clues on terrestrial magnetism. Here may lie the explanations for shifts in Earth's magnetic field, wandering of the north and south magnetic poles, and perhaps even the suspected wandering of the continents. The core is now believed to be the source of many magnetic phenomena.

We usually think of Earth as very hard and solid, and therefore rigid. Solid it may be, mostly, but rigid—no. It can be compared to a much-cracked fresh egg whose contents are being slowly stirred. It can hold to its nearly spherical form only because the forces acting upon it from outside—the pull of Sun and Moon—are so gentle. Even so, it gets out of balance as material on its crust gets moved here and there by erosion. Beneath the crust, plastic and liquid rock is probably in motion constantly, in response to changes in pressure from the crust and perhaps in response to changes of internal temperatures also. Inside as well as out, our Earth is a world of change.

Folded rocks—*Face of Mt. Timpanogos, northeastern Utah, shows signs of tremendous thrusting forces that raised mountains here fifty million years ago.*

Faulted rocks—*Close-up of banded sandstone strata shows how rock masses deep in Earth have cracked and shifted. Movement in crust never ceases.*

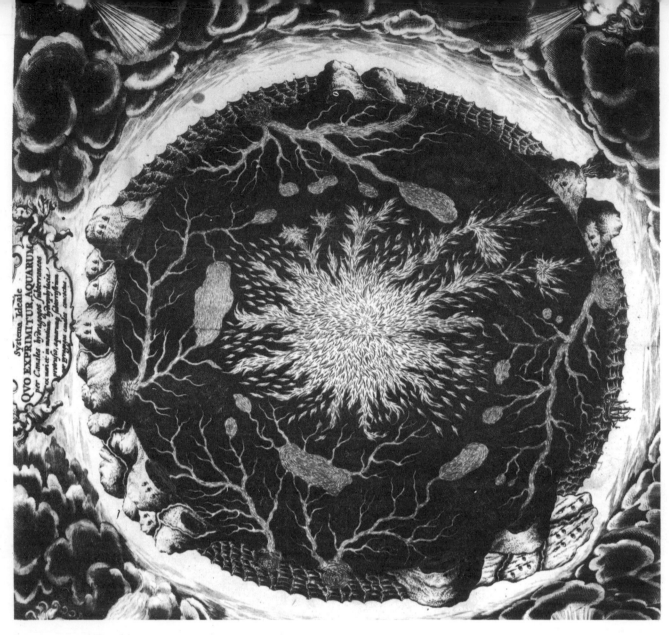

Earth's interior: 17th-century view—*Drawing in Kircher's* Mundus Subterraneus, *1664, shows imagined great fire at center, vast caverns, channels through which water sinks through sea bottoms and rises into mountains, and formation of volcanoes.*

Reading the Rocks

EARTH AS we understand it is very different from Earth as viewed by our ancestors. Until little more than a century ago, geological events were commonly regarded as the works of gods and spirits, usually fickle and not always friendly toward man. Even the greatest philosophers had little inkling of how the world was created and how it has changed since. Today a schoolboy can soon learn to recognize, and to understand in a general way, the grand patterns of geological change. And he will see them as the interrelated workings of natural forces.

Our twentieth-century view was not reached by one swoop of genius. It was reached by long, insistent groping for the reasons why things happen as they do. All geological events were once a puzzle (and some still are). Only patient observation, and careful reasoning based on it, could give us knowledge that will stand the test of reality. That knowledge is still in the making.

What, then, were some of the old ideas about Earth, and by what steps has the science of geology come into being?

In ancient times, there was no shortage of thinkers who asked How? and Why? Most of their thinking was about religious matters, but some were definitely curious about such Earthly matters as mountains and rocks, volcanoes and earthquakes, fossils and rivers.

The Greek thinker Ptolemy guessed that Earth is a ball, with a gigantic furnace inside. The famed Greek philosopher Aristotle explained that rocks form from effects of sunlight and starlight on the crust. This world-famous teacher, whose ideas reigned over our civilization for two thousand years, taught that earthquakes and volcanoes are caused by violent winds underground.

As recently as a few hundred years ago, scholars believed Earth to be flat. They said mountains are raised up by the "pull" of starlight. They suspected that fossils are the secret writings of spirits in the rocks, and whole books were written to describe how minerals form in the bodies—so it was said—of animals and plants. Rivers, said the scholars, are formed by water that runs down through holes in the bottom of the ocean, flows underground up into the mountains, and then pours down over the land to the ocean again.

These thinkers of the old days were intelligent men. But they had little real information to work with. They had not yet learned the value of careful observation. Instead of trying to *discover* causes of natural events, they would *think up* causes. That was not the road to knowledge.

ANSWERS IN THE ROCKS

But a few hundred years ago, here and there in Europe, a number of people were looking at the world and thinking about it in a new way. They were trying to trace out and describe a natural world of cause and effect.

In Poland, Nicholas Copernicus carefully watched the changing positions of Sun, planets, and stars. Before he died, in 1543, he declared

Anatomy of volcano—*Drawing of Vesuvius in* Kircher's Mundus Subterraneus *represents old idea that volcanoes result from tremendous fires burning underground.*

that Earth revolves about the Sun, not the Sun about Earth. In 1609 Galileo Galilei, the Italian, who loved to experiment, made himself a small telescope, used it to explore the heavens, and decided Copernicus was right. In the same year, Johannes Kepler, the German, came forward with formulas to explain the motions of the planets around the Sun. And as the century closed, Isaac Newton, the Englishman, was studying gravitation and the laws of motion.

By the middle of the 1700's, certain questioning men were looking at the crust of Earth just as others had studied the heavens. They, too, were beginning to understand natural cause and effect. And so they began to glimpse answers to some of the old questions.

Vast areas of the world, they noticed, are covered with bedrocks that obviously were once molten—so hot that they flowed. Could it be that much of our planet's surface was formed in fire?

Some observers saw how frost forces rocks apart, how weather works upon their surfaces,

25

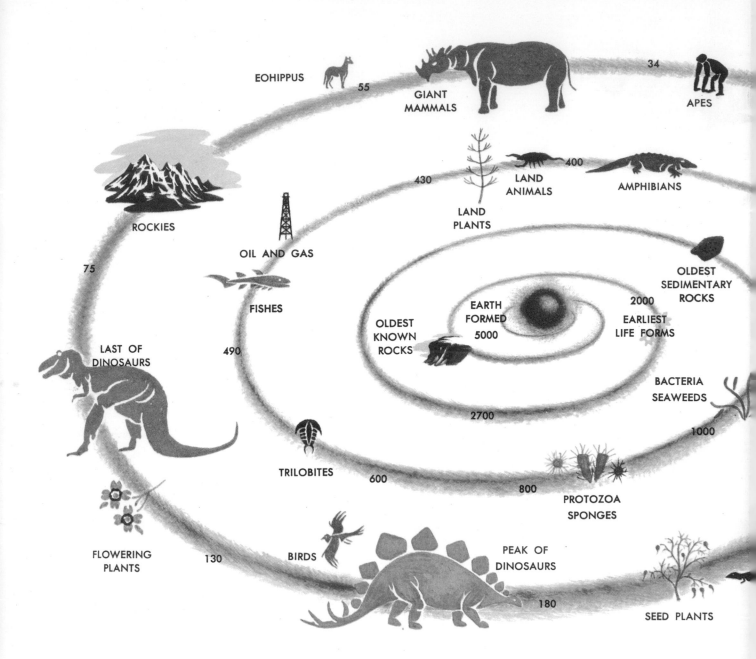

EOHIPPUS 55
GIANT MAMMALS
34
APES
ROCKIES
430
LAND PLANTS
LAND ANIMALS
400
AMPHIBIANS
OIL AND GAS
OLDEST SEDIMENTARY ROCKS
75
FISHES
2000
EARTH FORMED 5000
OLDEST KNOWN ROCKS
EARLIEST LIFE FORMS
LAST OF DINOSAURS
490
BACTERIA SEAWEEDS
2700
1000
TRILOBITES 600
800
PROTOZOA SPONGES
FLOWERING PLANTS
130
BIRDS
PEAK OF DINOSAURS
180
SEED PLANTS

and how running water carves gullies down hillsides and across fields. Could it be that whole valleys have been carved—whole mountain ranges sculptured—in this way?

Over parts of Earth's crust lie layers of rock, sometimes miles thick, that look as if they had formed in water. Some look a little like hardened clay or sand on the bottom of a dried-up pond. Could these bedrocks be hardened masses of rock particles and other waste dropped, through long ages, by rivers, lakes, and seas?

In rocks of high mountains—the Himalayas, the Alps, the Rockies—lie fossils of fish, seaweeds, and other things that surely at some time lived in

an ocean. Did movements in Earth's crust raise sea bottoms to make mountain ranges?

If fossils are the remains of living things, could a study of fossils build up a *connected* story of life in the past, from the algae of the original seas to modern man?

THE BIRTH OF GEOLOGY

Such possibilities overwhelmed the imagination. Yet it became clear that they were the truth. And still another important fact became plain: the slow-working forces that shaped the face of Earth as we see it today are still at work, preparing the Earth of tomorrow.

26

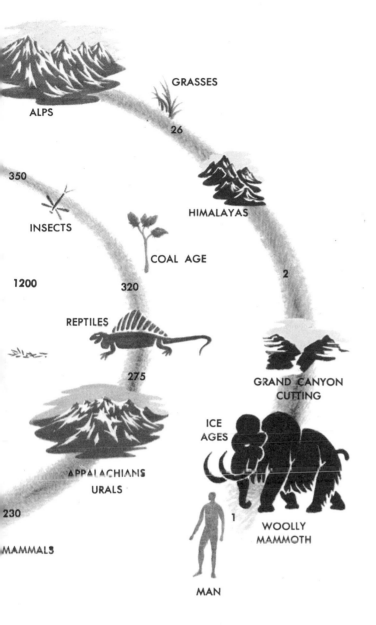

ALPS

GRASSES

26

350

INSECTS

HIMALAYAS

COAL AGE

1200   320

2

REPTILES

275

GRAND CANYON
CUTTING

ICE
AGES

APPALACHIANS
URALS

230

1

WOOLLY
MAMMOTH

MAMMALS

MAN

doubt concerning time. Many careful thinkers simply could not believe that Earth is as old as geologists said.

THE GULF OF TIME

In ancient Babylonia, four thousand years ago, priests had imagined Earth as created out of chaos two million years before. A lot could happen in that length of time. But thinkers of modern times, studying ancient history and the Bible, had guessed Earth to be much younger. Perhaps ten thousand—maybe fifty thousand years—seemed more likely. What we call civilization had begun only six thousand years before!

Could whole mountain ranges be worn down, mile-deep bedrocks formed, canyons sliced thousands of feet through rock—even in fifty thousand years?

Such were the doubts. But, as the 1800's rolled on, the truth was gradually unveiled. The secret of Earth *is* time. All the evidence that geologists could put together pointed to the enormous span of years covered by geological processes.

Someone estimated the amount of salt in the oceans of the world. This salt was known to have been dissolved out of the land and poured into the seas by rivers down through the ages. How long had this process taken? The answer seemed to be—millions of years.

Geologists climbed mountain ranges, measured the folded layers of rock, and calculated how much of these ranges had been eroded away. They estimated the present rates of erosion and figured how long it would take for these ranges to be worn down to their present levels. The reasonable answer seemed to be—tens of millions of years.

How long does it take for bedrocks, geologists asked, to form from grains of rock and other wastes of Earth's crust? Rates of formation vary a great deal from place to place. But suppose we put the average for limestone in the Grand Canyon

Thus began the science of Earth's crust: the science of geology. Like other sciences, it grew rapidly during the nineteenth century. Alert, curious men tramped over Europe and the British Isles, North America, Africa and South America, the oceanic islands, and Asia, reading the rocks as they went. They looked, measured, compared. Facts were put together like pieces of a jigsaw puzzle. Gradually, as that jigsaw puzzle was put together, it became a vast panorama of Earth changes, past and present.

Yet there remained doubts that Earth's history could be explained by processes that are still going on. And the most serious doubt of all was the

original cold mass or from a molten mass—must have required four to five billion years.

Truly, the secret of Earth *is* time.

THE WRECK OF FORMER WORLDS

We live amid the wreck of former worlds.

Earth's crust is the ruin of ancient landscapes and seascapes, of mountains and meadows and oceans. It is the graveyard of all the living things of the past, and the wreck of their dwelling places.

at a foot every three thousand years. The layers of exposed limestone there total about 1,500 feet!

The theory of evolution, too, pointed to an enormous time span for Earth. According to Charles Darwin and his followers, living things have developed from simple, one-celled creatures to the marvelously complicated beings we call man. But evolution is extremely slow—so slow that during all human history we have seen very little change in the animals and plants that inhabit Earth. To explain the countless changes in living forms as revealed by fossils in the rocks, millions and *millions* of years are needed.

As the twentieth century opened, many geologists had decided that the planet's age must be something like a hundred million years. But their measuring methods had been inexact. A more reliable method, involving radioactivity tests, was developed by nuclear physicists. This indicated an age of more than two billion years for the oldest known rocks.

At this point, yet another group of scientists stepped forward: the astronomers. They had been using the great new telescopes to observe physical changes in the Sun and other stars. The Sun, they calculated, has been burning its hydrogen supplies for ten to fifteen billion years. Earth, to reach its present stage of development—whether from an

Wreck of former worlds—*Monument Valley, Arizona, like all other landscapes of our planet, is ruin of earlier landscapes.*

28

Such magnificent works of destruction as the Grand Canyon of the Colorado, or the badlands of South Dakota and Wyoming, are easy to recognize as "wrecks." But the rounded old granite hills of New England, the gentle slopes of Ohio, the wheat-clad plains of Kansas and the duned beaches of Florida—these, too, are the wreck of former worlds.

These worlds are almost unimaginably remote in time. A few comparisons will help to show *how* remote these worlds really are:

Geologists say the Colorado River has taken about two million years to cut the Grand Canyon. That is twice as long as the whole span of man's existence on Earth. It is several hundred times as long as all written human history.

The Appalachian Mountains rose up 300 to 250 million years ago. They are about fifty thousand times as old as the Pyramids.

The dinosaurs were at their peak about 100 million years ago. That is ten thousand times as long ago as the close of the last ice age.

Imagine a limestone forming on an ocean bottom at the rate of a foot every three thousand years. In the twenty centuries of the Christian calendar, only nine inches of that stone has formed.

This is how, as we read the rocks, we can begin to think of geologic time.

The Zone of Fire

The notion that Earth was born in fire appears in the legends of primitive peoples and in the beliefs of ancient philosophers. Fire has been ever fascinating, and often terrifying, to man. It was easy to believe that the greatest of all imaginable events, the creation of the world, must have been governed by fire.

Most people have never seen a volcano—or, for that matter, a geyser, a hot spring, or a fumarole. Few parts of the world's surface show obvious signs of the fire that the ancients said burns eternally inside our globe. So in modern times observant people have found it hard to believe, in a very real sense, that volcanoes or any other manifestation of heat has been important in shaping the world. In fact, it was only a century and a half ago that a few observant men, the founders of geology, began to suspect how important in Earth history fire really has been.

NEPTUNISTS AND PLUTONISTS

During the early 1800's, a time of rapidly growing knowledge in science, the Earth was being examined with keener interest than ever before. Refusing to believe that the world had been created as it is in one grand act by a divine hand, men were beginning to say that our planet, however created in the first place, had since gone through a long series of changes. And the hills and valleys and rocks were being closely inspected for clues to this past.

Soon after 1800 a bitter argument was raging about how the bedrocks had formed. On one side were the Neptunists, named after the sea god Neptune because they believed the bedrocks had formed from water, as mud hardens on the bottom of a dried-up pond. Opposing them were the Plutonists, named after Pluto, god of the underworld and ruler of the globe's internal fires.

The Plutonists believed many of the bedrocks had once been molten.

The Neptunists, led by the German mineralogist Abraham Gottlob Werner, a famous and beloved teacher at the Freiberg Mining Academy, pointed impatiently at the sandstones, shales, and limestones. Did not many of these contain fossils of sea plants and animals? They must, therefore, have formed in water. The granites, basalts, and related bedrocks have no fossils; but they are

"Lunar" landscape—*Craters of Moon volcanic area in eastern Idaho has been active within recent centuries. It suggests desolate, crater-pitted face of Earth's satellite.*

often seen sandwiched between the other rocks, so they too must have formed on sea bottoms. In fact, according to Werner's teaching, the Earth began as a sphere covered entirely by a muddy ocean, and the bedrocks were created as the water cleared and the sediments dropped to the bottom.

Werner's beliefs seemed to have support from the Bible. Noah's Flood apparently explained not only the forming of rock in water but the rumpling and cracking often noticed in rock formations. (What a Flood it must have been!) Fossils were believed to be the remains of plants and animals trapped in the mud as the Flood waters dried up.

The Plutonists, on the contrary, declared that volcanic activity had produced many bedrocks, particularly the basalts and granites. As early as 1752, the French naturalist Jean Guettard had called attention to basalts among old lava flows

Did builder know? *The chapel St. Michel d'Aiguilhe, Le Puy, France, was built in 11th century 290 feet high atop hardened plug of ancient volcano. Plugs were favored sites for churches and castles.*

A FIERY HISTORY

For years the argument raged. Werner never gave in; but gradually his supporters dropped away. His most brilliant student, Leopold von Buch, took one good look at the Auvergne flows and joined the Plutonists. Werner never did go to see.

Von Buch, a man with tremendous curiosity, became the world's first great authority on volcanic activity. He showed that volcanoes do not result from the burning of coal, pitch, or other combustible substances underground, but are formed by molten material—far hotter than any burning coal—working up from the depths.

Von Buch and other Plutonists told the people of Europe a disturbing, even frightening truth. Many of the quiet landscapes around them had, indeed, formed in fire. Many mountains that had spouted flame in past ages were still standing, though worn and gentled by time. In some regions where no old volcanoes were to be seen, lava had simply burst from the depths and poured out over the land. In other places, molten rock had cooled and hardened underground, and later been uncovered by erosion. Almost any place might at *some* time have been the scene of volcanic activity. What had happened once could happen again!

in the mountains of Auvergne in southern France. Nicolas Demarest had studied these basalt formations and found that they were *parts of the flows.* Similar basalt rocks, said the Plutonists, have been noticed in Germany, Italy, Ireland, and Scotland, and so these, too, must be old volcanic regions. In fact, large areas of Earth must at some time have blazed with volcanoes!

Volcanic Region—*Cutaway shows how igneous activity in crust produces various landscape forms—volcano, surface lava flows, dikes and sills, laccoliths, geysers and hot springs, and fumaroles.*

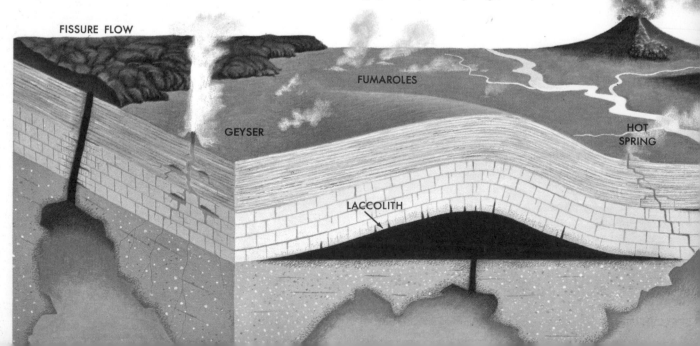

FISSURE FLOW

GEYSER

FUMAROLES

HOT SPRING

LACCOLITH

In time, popular fears quieted. Geologists learned that the volcanic remains scattered over the globe are from events that happened now and then *over a very long period of time*. Today no scientist fears that volcanoes will start bursting out all over the world at once.

But the discovery of Earth's fiery past was a great step for the young, growing science of geology. It explained the once-molten rocks and pointed the way to an understanding of how minerals form. It gave clues to forces that cause earthquakes, build mountains, and bend, fold, or break bedrocks. It was a big piece in the jigsaw puzzle of how Earth was created and what has happened to it since.

THE MAKING OF MAGMA

Volcanoes, lava flows, geysers, hot springs, and fumaroles are all forms of what geologists call "igneous activity." "Igneous" is from the Latin word *ignis,* meaning fire.

All igneous activity is caused by underground heat. Exactly where and how this heat is produced is not known, but much of it certainly comes from radioactive minerals. Over very long stretches of time these minerals "decay," or break up, into other substances. As they do so, heat is given off, just as it is by atomic reactors.

To this heat is added more heat from chemical reactions in Earth's crust. Still further heat is created, here and there, by friction, as big sections of the crust shift and rub against one another. Per-

haps some heat comes from the very core of the planet, which may be molten.

All this heat, plus pressure from the weight of the bedrocks, is constantly at work on the material that makes up the crust. Near the surface, this material is in the form of bedrocks, which consist of distinct minerals. Deeper down, heat and pressure probably keep the material in a "doughy" form, which geologists call magma. It may not consist of definite kinds of minerals as we know them. The minerals form one after another as the magma cools and gradually turns solid.

CRATER

CONE

SILL

DIKE

PIPE

Old Reliable—*Mt. Etna, Italy, highest volcano in Europe, has erupted intermittently since first recorded outburst, 475 B.C.*

A VOLCANO FORMS

Here and there, especially in mountain regions, magma forces its way upward through cracks in the crust and finally reaches the surface. There it may pour out over the ground as a lava flow. Or, if the upward flow of magma continues long enough, what we call a volcano may form.

A volcano consists essentially of the pipe, or channel, through which the magma rises, and the cone-shaped hill or mountain of volcanic material that piles up around the opening at the top.

As the magma comes up, it is very hot—around 1,800 degrees Fahrenheit. It is highly charged with gases, and can dissolve rocks and even metals. It may break off chunks of rock from its channel and carry these along. When it meets underground water, it changes this to steam, which is carried along too.

Volcanic ash heap—*Beds of lava dust blown out by Mt. Mazama, old volcano in Oregon, around 12,000 years ago, have been carved by running water into towers and pinnacles, some 200 feet high.*

MEDIUM-GRAINED GRANITE

QUARTZ

FELDSPAR

BIOTITE MICA

FINE-GRAINED GRANITE

RED GRANITE

Rocks That Cooled Underground

GABBRO

PEGMATITE

PERIDOTITE

DIORITE

GRANITE PORPHYRY

SYENITE

The magma changes as it rises. The higher it gets, the less material there is above it and the less weight there is on it. Also, it cools somewhat. This lessening of pressure and the cooling allow materials in the magma to start changing their forms.

Some that were liquid now rapidly turn to gases. But a substance in the form of a gas takes up much more space than when it is a liquid. Therefore, as the magma reaches the outer world, it is rapidly expanding. It foams like soda pop.

As it cools, the foaming mass tends to stiffen and rise less rapidly. That causes gas pressure to build up in the channel below. Then there may be explosions, just as a firecracker bursts from the pressure of burning gases inside.

THE FORMS OF LAVA

Magma reaching the surface becomes the bubbling molten rock called lava. Some flows out of the pipe in seething streams, and some is blown out.

Blown-out material includes big pear-shaped blobs called bombs and tiny lava droplets, or lapilli. There may be frothy bits of rock known as pumice, as well as clouds of lava dust, or "ash," and fragments of cooling lava called scoriae—full of holes made by escaping gases, and very light.

Now and then, volcanic "blocks" may be blasted out of the crater. These are chunks of rock torn loose from the volcano's pipe.

Most of the blown-out material falls near the vent, or opening, of the pipe. As eruptions go on, this material builds up to form a cone-shaped hill, with a crater in the top.

Lava that boils over the edge of the crater flows down the slopes of the cone. Lavas of the type that form the dark, so-called basalt rocks tend to flow more easily and go farther than the thicker, stiffer lavas which form rocks of the granite type.

Basalt lava flows usually cool into smooth-surfaced, often ropy or pillow-like masses. These masses, familiar in the Hawaiian Islands, have been given the Hawaiian name *pahoehoe*.

Quiet for now—*Ubehebe Crater, in Death Valley, California, is relic of geologically recent volcanism.*

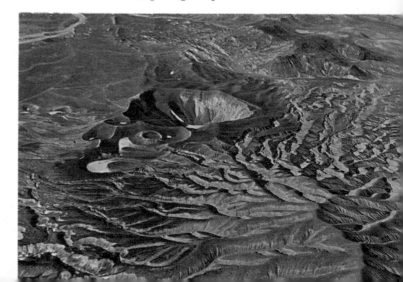

BASALT

BASALT
(arid-climate
weathering)

BASALT
(humid-climate
weathering)

PUMICE

ANDESITE

RHYOLITE

OBSIDIAN

AMYGDALOIDAL BASALT

SCORIA

Rocks That Cooled Aboveground

If the surface of a flow cools while the main mass is still moving inside, the surface may form a crust that breaks up into sheets and slivers. It is the worst thinkable stuff to walk on. Hawaiians call it *aa.*

Even after the surface of a flow has hardened, lava inside may continue to flow, like water through a pipe. When the flow does cool and stop, it may leave a partly empty channel called a volcanic tube. Erosion may later uncover part of this tube. Exploring it, we may find lava "stalactites" hanging from the ceiling, and "stalagmites" rising from the floor.

THE VOLCANIC CLOUD

A volcano in eruption usually produces a great, windy cloud—mostly condensed moisture. Mixed with it are carbon dioxide and perhaps hydrogen and nitrogen, hydrochloric acid gas, and yellow sulfur vapor.

Quick flames—bluish, greenish, or yellowish—may light the cloud as hydrogen combines with oxygen in the air to form water, and as the heat makes the sulfur and other materials burn. Tons of hydrochloric acid, formed from hydrogen and chlorine, may be swept over the countryside by gusts of wind. Carbon dioxide may flow down the mountain and into villages below, suffocating people as it did in Pompeii during the great eruption of A.D. 79. With it go clouds of irritating sulfur dioxide.

At intervals, lightning flashes through the cloud. The electricity is produced as bits of lava dust, violently blown around in the cloud, strike against one another, and also as steam condenses into droplets of water and chemicals react.

Volcanic clouds always contain a great deal of moisture. Water formed by condensing steam may rush down the mountainsides in torrents, picking up lava dust to form muddy floods.

"Ropes" and "pillows"—*Cooled lava flows at Craters of Moon, Idaho, show typical forms of pahoehoe. Similar lavas issuing from ocean bottoms take forms more like pillows.*

Sacred mountain—_Beautiful Fujiyama, on Honshu, Japan, typifies cone volcano. It last erupted in 1707._

CONE VOLCANOES

Some magmas contain more gas than others. These magmas form volcanoes that blow out much of their material as dust, scoriae, pumice, and bombs.

Dust may be carried many miles by winds, but most of the blown-out material falls back into the crater or near it. If the volcano produces lava that is stiff and cannot flow far, this also piles up near the crater. Thus is formed a volcanic cone that is quite steep-sided. The perfect example of this type of volcano is Mount Vesuvius, in Italy.

Now, a volcanic cone is put under great strain by magma rising in the pipe. The magma is heavy, and gases in it, trying to escape, press very hard against the inside of the cone. A steep cone sometimes cracks under this strain, and gases and lava burst through the cracks.

Cinder cones—_Here, on slopes of a mountain in the Andes of South America, recent volcanic activity made cones. Lava flow all but destroyed cone at upper left._

"Witch's caldron"—Paricutín nighttime activities attracted many photographers with color film. Volcano was visited by thousands of sightseers.

Free heat—*In New Zealand, steam plant was set up to make use of heat in volcanic Wairakei Valley. Volcanic heat is expensive to exploit, not widely used.*

That relieves pressure in the cone. But, as in our bottle of soda pop, great amounts of gas are released by the reduction of pressure. The release of gases may be so sudden and violent as to blow out the side of the cone.

Cone volcanoes, therefore, are often dangerous. But there are exceptions such as Mount Etna, in Italy. It has about two hundred fissures, perhaps acting as "safety valves." Small cones have formed along the fissures. These so-called parasitic cones draw magma from the main pipe.

The Americas have many cone volcanoes. One of them is Mount Lassen, in northern California, the only volcano in the United States considered active. It began erupting in 1914 and continued its activity until 1921. It has since been quiet.

Chile, in South America, has Cotopaxi. This is the highest volcano in the world—19,600 feet.

In Mexico there are many cones. One has the name that visitors like to pronounce: Popocatepetl. More famous is Paricutín—the only volcano studied by scientists practically from its birth.

THE SMOKING FIELD

Paricutín was born in 1943 in a mountainous region about 200 miles from Mexico City. Early in February, a series of earthquakes began here, and each day they grew worse. On February 20, a farmer saw a small column of "smoke" rising from his field. As frightened villagers watched, the column grew. By the next day it had become a large cloud, pouring out of a cinder cone 100 feet high. The cone grew as explosions, every few seconds, threw out showers of rocks and dust.

During the next few days, scientists arrived with notebooks, cameras, seismographs, and other equipment. As they looked on, the earth around the cone cracked and lava flows began. In time, some of the flows spread outward six miles.

Showers of rock chunks and scoriae built the cone to 500 feet in two weeks, 1,100 feet in three months, and 1,400 feet in the first year. On one day in 1945 the volcano belched out an estimated 16,000 tons of steam and 100,000 tons of lava.

All fields and woods for miles around were destroyed. Several villages were buried, including the town of Paricutín itself. Fortunately, the inhabitants had had enough warning to escape.

A.D. 79

The story was different for the people who were living near Mount Vesuvius, in Italy, in the year A.D. 79. In those days people did not recognize certain fateful warnings.

The mountain stands southeast of the blue bay of Naples. It is a very old mountain, and well known. Two thousand years ago—and even before that—farmers had planted vineyards and olive groves in the dark, fertile soils around the mountain and on its slopes. The mountain was green almost to the top, and vines and flowers grew even in the broad, circular hollow in the summit.

About A.D. 25, a Greek geographer and traveler, Strabo, visited this region. While walking high on the mountain he noticed patches of cinder-like material and scorched rock. After making a few scholarly notes, he went his way. Whether he talked to any of the farmers about the mountain, no one knows.

In the year A.D. 63, the region was shaken by a series of earthquakes. Several towns suffered much property damage. Hardest hit was the small city of Pompeii, near the foot of the mountain. This town of 20,000 was a resort of wealthy Romans, who came here to relax in their villas overlooking the sea. The city's Temple of Isis and other public buildings were leveled.

But where the soil is fertile and life is easy, people remain. Through sixteen years of occasional earthquakes, they remained around the mountain. Who would have dreamed that the cinder-like materials on the quiet slopes were a warning?

In August of A.D. 79 the quakes got worse. And on the 24th, the quiet old mountain spoke.

The south side of the summit—that place of vines and flowers—vanished. Gases and dust poured out in enormous black clouds that darkened the sky for miles. Down upon the towns swept gusts of poisonous gases, with showers of dust, hot rain, and mud. Terrified people fleeing through the streets were suffocated by the hundreds. Many were entombed in their homes as the swirling pumice, like a devil's blizzard, piled up to depths of fifteen and twenty feet.

The town of Herculaneum, near Pompeii, fared no better. Steam from the volcanic cloud condensed into heavy rains, which rushed down the slopes, mixed with thousands of tons of dust, and poured through the streets. The floods of hot mud did not stop until they had covered rooftops fifty to sixty-five feet high.

The mountain quieted, and the poisonous clouds blew away. All that remained was a smoking sea of mud and lava around the mountain's base, with a few blackened rooftops, and the mountain's plume of gases waving above all. In

"Quiet old mountain"—*Ruin of building in Pompeii frames Mt. Vesuvius, villain of many an old story.*

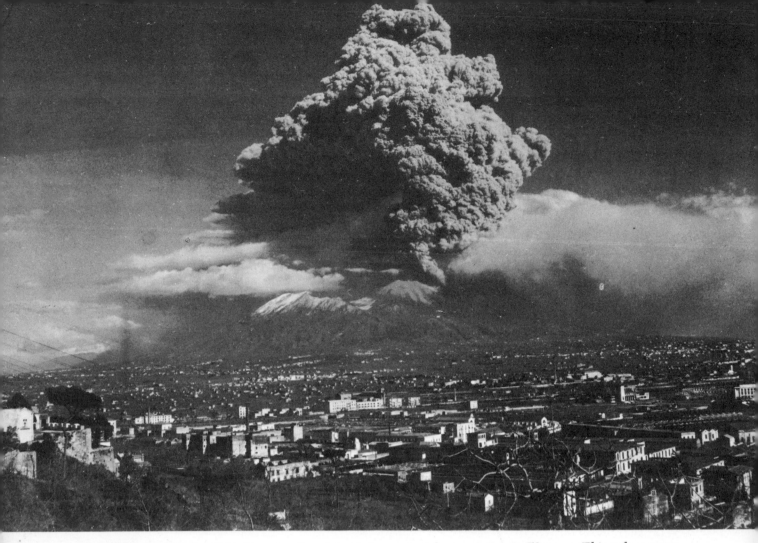

Awake again—*In 1944, Vesuvius burst forth in most violent eruption in 72 years. This volcano produces gassy, viscous, slow-flowing type of lava, which tends to cause sudden, destructive outbursts.*

Pompeii alone, no less than two thousand people were entombed.

SLEEPING FIRES

In every volcano's life, there comes a time when the upward flow of magma stops. Magma in the pipe cools and hardens, forming a plug. The volcano becomes dormant.

But a dormant volcano may be—as old Mount Vesuvius was—treacherous. Suppose the underground pressure starts building up again, and rising magma is stopped by the plug. Pressure keeps building up, there are earthquakes in the region, and at last the volcano may "blow."

Some of the most frightful disasters of history occurred when plugged volcanoes resumed business. This was the story several times with Vesuvius, and it happened with Krakatoa and Pelée.

The volcano on the island of Krakatoa, in Indonesia, exploded in 1883. Steam, pumice, and ashes were shot twenty to thirty miles high. Ships in Sunda Strait were showered with phosphorescent mud. A large part of the island was de-

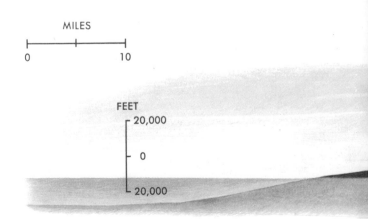

MILES

0   10

FEET

20,000

0

20,000

Mauna Loa: a shield volcano—*Diagram shows enormous expanse of lava flows built up on ocean floor. Height of Mauna Loa's crater above Pacific bottom is greater than height of Mt. Everest above sea level.*

Birth of an island—*Lava issuing from sea bottom near Japan rises above waves to form new land mass.*

stroyed, and earthquakes started a great sea wave that drowned 30,000 people on the islands of Java and Sumatra. About 4½ cubic miles of pumice were blown out—enough to make a block of stone four miles long, a mile wide, and more than a mile high. Dust blown into the stratosphere was carried by winds entirely around the world, and for many months it caused sunrises and sunsets of unusual redness.

Mount Pelée, on the island of Martinique in the West Indies, erupted in 1902 after fifty years of calm. The very stiff lava of this volcano was pushed out of the top as a tower about 1,000 feet high. Its enormous weight, added to the gas pressures beneath, made the side of the cone give way. Out of the hole shot a gigantic red-hot cloud of ash, sand, and steam. Flashing with lightning, it swept down over the countryside at sixty miles per hour. The town of St. Pierre, capital of Martinique, was engulfed, and all but one of the 28,000 inhabitants—a man who was safe underground in jail—were suffocated or burned to death. In the harbor, the waters boiled, and ships were overturned.

SHIELD VOLCANOES

Magma that produces free-flowing lava creates volcanoes of the "shield" type. The perfect model is Mauna Loa, in the Hawaiian Islands.

These islands were all born in fire. Here, in past ages, great cracks opened in the ocean floor, and white-hot basalt oozed forth. The ocean waters boiled and steamed. Layer upon layer, the lava piled up on the ocean bottom, forming underwater mountain ranges. The highest peaks rose above the waves, becoming the islands of today.

Mauna Loa grew up where a number of cracks came together. This volcano took perhaps a million years to build—much longer than the usual

Tourists' favorite—*Crater of Kilauea bubbles and spouts gently in 1952 eruption. Nearby crater Kilauea Iki (Little Kilauea) burst into activity in 1959.*

The great crater of Mauna Loa has recently been quiet. On the east side of the mountain, at an altitude of 4,000 feet, is the crater Kilauea. This has a pipe separate from Mauna Loa's and has been more recently active. Near Kilauea a geological observatory has been built, and here volcanologists keep a close watch on events.

IS THERE ANY WARNING?

Scientists have been studying volcanoes for over a hundred years. Observatories such as those on Vesuvius, Kilauea, and Mount Pelée have revealed many secrets of volcanic activity. Although eruptions have no particular schedule, the volcano experts have sometimes been able to predict trouble and to save life and property.

A fairly sure sign of trouble is a series of earthquakes near a volcano. These, with tilting of the ground, indicate that sections of the crust are shifting. New channels may be opening up for magma, and underground pressures are perhaps increasing. Wells in the area may go dry—indicating that cracks underground are allowing the water to leak deeper into the earth. Water reaching hot rocks, far down, may turn to steam and boost the pressures that are causing the quakes.

Lava issuing from a volcano, at a time of mild activity, can be studied for hints as to what is

cone volcano. The very fluid lava spread far before it cooled and stopped, so that the mountain did not develop steep sides. Instead, it has the form of a very broad, low heap—a shield.

The bottom of this enormous heap of basalt is seventy miles in diameter. The volcano's crater, 13,680 feet above the sea, is two miles long and a mile wide. Since the sea is in this region about 17,000 feet deep, the mountain rises more than 30,000 feet—that is, nearly six miles—above the ocean floor!

In 1935 a fast-moving lava flow threatened to engulf the nearby town of Hilo. United States Army bombers, called upon for help, bombed the flow to steer it away from the town.

Magma cools in cone as volcano becomes inactive

Hard plug is exposed as erosion strips away soft cone

Plug remains as "neck" long after cone is gone

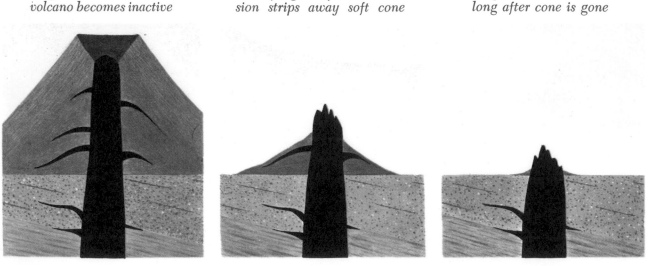

Fossil volcano—1,640-foot Ship Rock, New Mexico, is all that remains of giant plug of lava that cooled in throat of dying volcano. Cone has been eroded away. Plugs are common in many formerly volcanic regions.

going on in the hot depths. An eruption may be hinted also by changes in Earth's magnetism in the region.

WHEN VOLCANOES DIE

A volcano may be alive, as Vesuvius was, even after centuries of calm. It may be busy for a number of years, as Paricutín was, and then quiet down. Or it may perform practically without a halt for century after century. The volcano on the island of Stromboli, north of Sicily, has been popping mildly since the days of ancient Rome. Its friendly glow at night has earned it the name "Lighthouse of the Mediterranean."

Some volcanoes die, and the forces of erosion go to work. In time the cone or shield is worn low. More time passes, and then there is nothing left to hint at the fiery business of long ago.

A familiar relic of vanished volcanoes is the volcanic neck. This is the chunk of lava that cooled in the throat of the volcano as it died. When the cone of the volcano eroded away, the plug remained. But a plug left standing alone is not actually a plug any more; it is a "neck."

One of the San Francisco Peaks in northern Arizona, north of Flagstaff, is a volcanic neck. Another well-known neck is Ship Rock, in the northwestern corner of New Mexico—1,400 feet high. Running outward from the neck, like wheel spokes across the desert, are long arms of rock called dikes. These are made of magma that cooled in fissures below the volcano's cone.

Volcanic necks that rise high and steep above the surrounding countryside have been, in past times, favorite sites for the erection of fortifications and religious buildings. Picturesque Edinburgh Castle, in Scotland, and the charming little chapel of St. Michel in the Auvergne province, in France, were both built on necks.

Perhaps the best-known volcanic relic of the western United States is Crater Lake in Oregon, the site of ancient Mount Mazama. Some 6,500 years ago this mountain, then about 12,000 feet high, blew around 10 cubic miles of pumice into the sky. The material came from the inside of the crater, and its walls, much weakened, fell in. An enlarged, saucer-shaped crater was thus formed—a "caldera." Today the caldera is six miles in diameter and 4,000 feet deep, and is filled with the waters of the lake. Above the lake rises the cinder cone known as Wizard Island, which was produced by eruptions after the caldera formed.

Numerous old cinder cones are seen today in the West. In the Craters of the Moon area of north-central Idaho there are many up to 600 feet high. There are more in northeastern New Mexico, Arizona, and California.

FISSURE FLOWS

Lava that reaches Earth's surface through long cracks, rather than a pipe, may not form volcanoes. It may simply flow out over the land in wide, bubbling rivers. Much of the igneous activity in our planet's history has been of this sort.

Volcano that became a lake—*Collapse of crater of Mt. Mazama, about 12,000 years ago, left caldera now occupied by Crater Lake, 2,000 feet deep. Wizard Island (right center) is cinder cone formed in recent times. Inset suggests probable shape of mountain before crater collapsed.*

Such flows may be quite as disastrous as big volcanic eruptions. Iceland, for example, once suffered frightful damage and loss of life from one of these fissure flows. Iceland lies in a long region of volcanic activity arching over the north Atlantic and down to the Azores and Canary Islands. In 1783, fast-moving basaltic lava poured out of a fissure twenty miles long and spread outward twenty to forty miles on each side. A fifth of Iceland's population were wiped out.

THE LAVA SEAS

The fissure flow in Iceland was nothing compared to some flows that occurred before the age of man. In the northwestern United States there is a plateau, or highland, of basalt that covers areas of five states—Washington, Oregon, Idaho, Nevada, and California. Here the Snake and Columbia Rivers have cut their way through the basalt to depths of 4,000 feet. The entire basalt area covers about 200,000 square miles, or more than four times the area of New York State. The amount of lava poured out in the various flows here was about 100,000 cubic miles—equal to a solid block 100 miles on each side and 10 miles high. Valleys nearly a mile deep were filled.

The remains of a mass of basalt covering 600,000 square miles form a broad, curving path reaching from Greenland through Iceland, to the Inner Hebrides near Scotland, and down to Antrim in Northern Ireland. These flows, as much as 1,500 feet thick, lie mostly under the ocean.

One of the thickest lava beds ever discovered is in the Lake Superior region. The basalt here is 50,000 feet deep in places—nearly 10 miles. Part of this frozen lava sea forms the Keweenaw Peninsula, famous for its copper.

UNDERGROUND FLOWS

Some flows of magma are halted before they reach the earth's surface. The molten stuff cools and hardens underground. Long afterward, erosion may uncover it.

Magma may force its way between rock layers and there cool as a sheet or slab, which geologists call a sill. A famous sill is the Palisades formation along the Hudson River northwest of New York City. This block of basalt runs fifty miles northward. Some 200 million years of erosion have worn away the softer rock in the region, leaving the harder basalt as high as 1,000 feet at points.

As magma forces its way between rock layers near the surface, the top layers may bulge up-

Land of Lava—*Near Grand Coulee Dam, in state of Washington, Columbia River cuts into old lava flows.*

upward into fractures, or cracks, *through* the layers. Dikes and sills are common in volcanic regions.

Very large underground magma reservoirs revealed by erosion are called batholiths, or plutons. These consist always of granite-type rocks—never basalt. All of them formed very long ago in the cores of mountain ranges, and they have been exposed only by many millions of years of erosion. These giant masses of frozen granite may be sedimentary rock, such as sandstone or shale, that melted as the mountains formed.

In Idaho a great pluton is exposed over an area of 16,000 square miles. Even larger is the Coast Mountains pluton of western Canada and Alaska. It is 1,200 miles long and 80 to 120 miles wide.

HOT SPRINGS AND FUMAROLES

Hot springs are of water that has passed over hot rock underground. The water is mostly rainwater that has worked its way down through cracks. Because of heat and pressure, the water is able to dissolve more minerals than it could normally. These minerals may give the springs medicinal value, and so areas where there are hot springs of the right kind become resorts. Hot Springs, Arkansas, is one such resort. Japan and New Zealand are famous for their hot springs.

Fumaroles are surface fissures through which gases rise from magma far below. While underground, the gases are so hot that they can dissolve even metals, such as iron, copper, and lead. As the gases escape at the surface, they cool and leave coatings of minerals on the ground. In this way some fumaroles produce valuable amounts of metallic ores, as well as sulfur and several useful gases.

Famous fumarole regions include Yellowstone National Park and the Valley of Ten Thousand Smokes in Alaska. There are fumaroles in Death Valley, California, too. Here carbon dioxide issuing from the fumaroles settles in low places in the valley, because this gas is heavier than air. Travelers there must be careful.

ward. The cooled magma then becomes what is called a laccolith. The La Sal Mountains of Utah are formed entirely of laccoliths uncovered by erosion. Many laccoliths are found also in the Henry Mountains of Utah.

Whereas sills are formed by magma working its way *between* rock layers, the formations called dikes are formed where the magma works its way

"Liberty Cap"—*Odd dome in Yellowstone National Park consists of minerals deposited by fumarole.*

Classic geyser—Old Faithful, in Yellowstone National Park, was named for its custom of erupting at approximately hourly intervals, year after year.

THE ANATOMY OF GEYSERS

One of the familiar and beautiful sights in some volcanic regions is the geyser. Every American has heard of Old Faithful, which spouts 15,000 gallons of steam and boiling water 150 feet into the air every 65 minutes or so.

Beneath every geyser is a looping channel, running down into a region of very hot rock. Underground water leaks into this channel and is heated by the rock. For a while, the weight of the water in the channel keeps the very hot water, far down, from changing to steam. Finally, however, some of the water gets so hot that it changes to steam anyway. The steam, because it takes up much more space than the water did, starts pushing upward in the channel and forces the higher water ahead of it.

Water now starts to gurgle out of the top, and makes room for more steam to form below. This

Why geysers perform—*Underground channels fill with ground water. Eruption occurs when water near bottom becomes hot enough to change to steam.*

new steam joins in the push, more water is thrown out at the top, more steam forms below—and suddenly most of the water in the channel has turned into steam and shot out of the top.

Then the empty channel starts filling again, preparing for a new eruption.

UNDERGROUND UPSET

A region of fumaroles, geysers, and hot springs is subject to sudden changes. In Yellowstone National Park, for example, the system of underground channels was badly disrupted by the earthquake of August 1959, centered nearby. Hot springs became geysers; geysers turned into hot springs; and some of these features went out of business entirely. Even Old Faithful changed its timetable.

The Shaping of the Land

THE FACE of Earth, in some regions, looks like a gigantic wreck. Rugged mountains, steep-cliffed canyons, great valleys gouged out of the land—these seem to suggest an ancient time when frightful earthquakes broke and rumpled the land. No wonder people believed for so long that the surfaces of our planet were formed by cataclysms.

The scientist knows that most of our landscapes have been shaped slowly, over millions of years—shaped by forces that are at work still.

As ages pass, sections of the crust gradually rise and sink, warp and fold. Water, air, and gravity keep wearing down the higher land and carrying it, bit by bit, down to the lower places.

Such processes account for landscapes as different as the Grand Canyon, the badlands of South Dakota and Wyoming, the sharply carved seacoasts of Maine and Oregon, and the rolling countryside of Ohio.

It is mainly the slow workers—water, air, gravity—that make our world.

A WORLD OF CHANGE

Less than two centuries ago, most educated people believed that the Earth is only about six thousand years old—an age that some scholars calculated from the Bible. Except for Noah's Flood, they believed, Earth has been much the same since creation.

"Magic City of Spires"—Bryce Canyon, southern Utah, testifies magnificently to power of running water in shaping land. Climate is dry; but when rain does come, vegetation here is insufficient to prevent rapid gullying in soft rocks. View is from Inspiration Point, a favorite lookout.

Such beliefs are hardly surprising. Except where there are great floods and volcanic outbursts—rare occurrences—landscapes change little during the lifetime of a person or even a nation. The rocky outlines of the hills are much the same as they were in the time of one's grandfather, in the time of Julius Caesar, and in the time when man was chipping his tools out of stone. The forces that change the look of the land work so slowly, so quietly, that they are easy to overlook altogether.

The powers of water to erode the land had been noticed by Aristotle and other ancients. But the first observer to grasp the full meaning of erosion was a Scottish physician, James Hutton, who had turned farmer and, with a scientist's curiosity, had been investigating the rocks and soils around him. In the cliffs he counted the varied strata and sampled their fossils. He observed the destructive power of the sea along the shores, and he watched rivers at work. To him the world seemed the wreckage, the refuse, of many, many thousands of years of erosion.

Hutton published in 1795 one of the great early books on geology: *Theory of the Earth*. He pictured Earth as possibly hundreds of thousands of years old—old enough for the forces of erosion to wear away the mountains again and again, washing their remains into the sea, from which new mountains would rise again. Even now these forces were at work, and men too might become fossils for future ages.

It was an awesome picture—this Earth so old that it seemed to have no beginning, no prospect of an end. Such an idea, contrary to human experience, could not win even educated men's minds for many years. A generation after Hutton, the eloquent and famous Sir Charles Lyell, father of British geology, was still trying to convince his scientific colleagues of the truth about erosion.

49

Today, with a century of geological science behind us, it is still not easy to think of the hills, valleys, and plains as the wreck of former worlds. But we can make a beginning.

WEARING DOWN A HILL

Could a granite hill rust? Could it crumble away like an old tin can outdoors?

Water, with oxygen from the air, will rust a tin can. Water and air will keep eating away at a granite hill, softening and crumbling it, grain by grain. A granite hill does not actually rust, but in time it *does* crumble away like an old tin can.

Our granite hill—any hill—is under attack by many forces. Plant roots feeling their way through the soil touch the rock, and chemicals in the roots corrode it. Rainwater, captured by the roots, is held against the rock and dissolves a slight amount of it. Roots work into cracks and widen them, just as tree roots raise a sidewalk.

Animals on the hill do their part, too. Some may burrow into the hill. Body wastes from ani-

Erosion of granite—At Sylvan Lake, near The Needles (above), eroded granite has rounded forms. When erosion here is advanced, thousands of years hence, remains of lake walls may be in form of needles.

Stumps of a mountain—*Long erosion has cut down sedimentary rock folds forming Sheep Mountain in Bighorns, Wyoming. Stumps of folds are "hogbacks." Inset suggests original form of mountain.*

mals corrode the rocks a little. Decaying plants and animals corrode rock surfaces a little more.

Even temperature changes are rock destroyers. When the Sun shines on rocks all day, heat works down into them. They expand with the heat— slightly, but definitely. Then the Sun sets and the air becomes rapidly cooler, or perhaps cool rain begins falling. The outside of the rock tries to shrink slightly while the inside is still warm. But that is like trying to put a small shoe on a big foot. Shrinking rock surfaces crack, and flakes or "shells" fall off.

WATER TRICKS

When water freezes, it expands, so that the ice takes up about one-ninth more space than the water did. The force of this expansion is tremen-

Rock honeycomb—*Percolation of water through soluble rock may produce patterns like this in limestone.*

dous; it can split boulders weighing tons. So when water freezes in cracks on the granite hill, it makes the cracks wider and breaks loose big chunks of rock.

When rain falls on the hill, it runs over the rocks. Having picked up some carbon dioxide and oxygen from the air, the water can dissolve certain minerals that pure rainwater could not dissolve. It dissolves a very little of the granite.

As drops of water run together, they form little rills. These rills pick up tiny bits of loose stone and carry them along. Where the rills run into the gullies, they form streams strong enough to carry or roll pebbles. The bits of rock and the pebbles, scraping larger rocks over which they travel, break off still more rock particles and carry these along. And so the destruction goes on as the rills join in the gullies to make brooks, and as the brooks run down into the valley to form rivers.

WATER WORKING EVERYWHERE

It takes millions of years to wear away a granite hill. But where the rocks are softer, or where only loose soil covers them, erosion is faster.

Everyone has seen what a heavy rain can do to a bank of bare sand or clay along a highway. Farmers dread the heavy rains that may cut gullies down through sloping fields. In our own backyards, we have seen tiny canyons cut by the rain.

The regions called badlands show amazing work done by water. In North America, these grim yet beautiful landscapes are found especially in the Dakotas, Nebraska and Wyoming, and Alberta. They look as if giant claws, not water, had raked through the earth's crust, cutting and breaking it into gorges, towers, and tumbled blocks.

These badlands are in regions of relatively light rainfall. There is little vegetation except for scattered desert plants. When rain does fall, there are few roots to capture water. It collects in gullies and

Once a fertile field—*Farmland near Tyre, Mississippi, shows results of uncontrolled gullying. Once started, gullying can become very rapid.*

dashes downward, cutting deeper and deeper through the soft shales and sandstones. One rain in the badlands causes more erosion than years of rains on a land of forested hills.

MESAS, MONUMENTS, AND GOBLINS

Especially in badlands, we find rocks eroded into strange forms—mesas, natural bridges, towers, "monuments," and "goblins."

The main reason for such forms is uneven erosion, due to differences in the resistance of rocks. As the surface of a region is gradually cut away, the soft rocks are destroyed faster than the hard ones. The harder rock formations are left standing out prominently, and wind-blown sand may smooth their surfaces.

"Goblins"—*Forms cut and polished by water and wind in Devil's Garden, near Escalante, Utah, suggest goblins in conversation. Note human figure.*

Sculptured by water—*Forbidding but beautiful are the bleak ruins called "badlands," created in dry regions by gullying in soft rock. This scene is in Badlands National Monument, South Dakota. Spectacular badlands occur in arid parts of other Western states as well as Africa, Middle East, and China.*

Lava pinnacles—*Water and weather carved these forms out of old rhyolite lava formation, Chiricahua National Monument, Arizona. Note size of man.*

Rock towers and other odd forms have like histories. A cap of hard rock protects soft layers beneath it. But these layers, too, are of differing hardness. So, as the centuries go by, all sorts of shapes may be carved out.

GRAVITY, THE LEVELER

Every particle of stone on a hill is being pulled by gravity. When a scampering chipmunk kicks a few bits of stone, most of them land farther downhill than they were before. A brief shower carries some of them an inch—others a hundred feet—farther downhill. A small snowslide in winter provides another downward ride. The blowing force of wind, the wedging force of ice, the force that swells and shrinks rocks as the temperature changes—all these join to keep the rock material on the hill moving downward.

Gravity is determined to bring everything on earth down to one level. Even in a billion years it will not forget one grain of stone for one second.

Around the base of a steep, rocky hill you may find heaped broken rock, perhaps partly covered with soil. This is rock waste pulled down by grav-

A mesa is commonly a block of rock layers with a hard protecting layer on top. Wind-blown rain and sand, as well as frost, keep chiseling away at the edges of the soft layers. Thus the hard layer is gradually undermined, gravity keeps breaking off its edges, and the mesa slowly shrinks.

Hogback: *Erosion of softer rocks leaves harder stratum as ridge.*

Dome: *Flaking off, common in granite, leaves dome.*

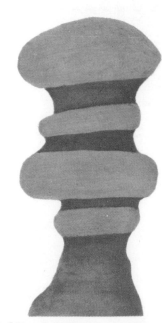

Mesa: *Hard cap rock protects softer rock beneath.*

Needles: *Work of frost in cracks may make needles.*

Goblin: *Soft layers are worn away faster than hard ones.*

Delicate Arch—*Natural bridges and similar structures, such as this one at Arches National Monument, Utah, are but chance creations of erosion.*

ity. Geologists call it a talus slope. Rock waste is here at rest—temporarily. Some day, gravity will find a way to move it still lower.

WHY LANDSLIDES?

Gravity works slowly on a granite hill. In other places it may work with shocking swiftness.

Take, for example, a hillside with a rather thick layer of clay lying on steeply sloping bedrock. Clay tends to get greasy and slippery when wet. After heavy rains, the clay layer begins to slip. Faster it moves, and faster—and we have a landslide, piling up thousands of tons of clay below.

Rivers, by undermining a hill or a cliff, may touch off landslides. A shift in Earth's crust, causing a

Tilted strata plus water plus gravity—*Landslide, Pacific Palisades, California, occurred where tilted shale strata were "lubricated" by period of heavy rain. Slides may be started by slight earthquakes.*

55

Erosion trick—Big Balanced Rock in Garden of the Gods, near Colorado Springs, Colorado, was actually shaped from rock mass by water and windblown sand. Many "balanced" rocks have like origin.

fault or crack, may do the same. Frost-wedging and the melting of heavy snows are other causes.

Man himself may be the cause of landslides. Blasting in mines and quarries has started numerous slides. After man has cleared a hill of trees and brush, there are few roots to soak up rain and anchor the soil, and slides become more likely. The cutting of roads and canals through hills also may lead to slides.

Some hills are formed of folded layers of bedrock, tilted steeply and cracked. If water works its way in between the layers, the outer ones may begin to slip. This is what happened some years ago in the Gros Ventre range, near the little town of Kelly, Wyoming.

The Gros Ventres are low, rounded mountains topped with soft red sandstone and shale. During 1925 there were heavy rains, and the water worked down through the soft strata. In June 1925 a great mass of the red stuff slid down into the valley of the Gros Ventre River.

The river, partly blocked by earlier slides, had formed Slide Lake. For two years this lake kept rising behind the higher dam formed by the new slide. By May 1927 it was three miles long.

Then, suddenly, the dam gave way, and a tremendous torrent of water rushed down through the little valley of the Gros Ventre and swept through Kelly. Houses were washed away, and several townspeople were drowned—as well as many livestock. Today Slide Lake is smaller, and all is peaceful, but in the slope above the lake one still sees the hollow—a great red scar—left by the great slide a generation ago.

TURTLE MOUNTAIN

The worst of all North American landslides was the one that occurred near the small town of Frank, in Alberta, Canada, in 1903.

Above Frank, which is a little coal-mining town, rises Turtle Mountain. The upper part of the moun-

Talus—*Tremendous accumulations of debris on lower slopes of mountains at Logan Pass, Glacier National Park, Montana, result mainly from wedging by frost.*

tain is formed of limestone layers that slant down steeply toward the town. The layers are much cracked, and the spaces between them have been widened by ice wedging and by the work of underground water.

Early one morning in 1903, men were blasting in the coal mine near the base of the mountain. All at once there was a trembling of the earth—not from the blasting. High on the steep side of the mountain, a block of limestone a half mile square and several hundred feet thick was slipping. Before the town knew what was happening, the gigantic stone block plunged downward.

Shattering as it hit the valley, like a breaking wave the block roared over part of the town and crashed against the opposite side of the valley a full two miles away.

In less than two minutes it was all over. There were seventy dead and missing in Frank. The miners, underground, were all unhurt.

In the Alps, where mountains are high, rock layers tilted, and frost active, similar landslides are common. Also common are snow avalanches. In spring, the time of melting, ice and rock under the great layers of snow become slippery. Even the touch of a breeze or the sound of a voice may jar the snow layers enough to start a slide.

For people in some Alpine villages, the experience of digging out home, family, and friends—alive or dead—is all too familiar.

Dammed by mudflow—Mass of rain soaked volcanic dust in San Juan Mountains, Colorado, flowed five miles down valley, blocked canyon of Gunnison River, and formed Lake San Cristobal. Flow (background) was dubbed "Slumgullion."

GONE WITH THE WIND

Winds carry sand and rock dust from one place to another. Desert winds, year after year, keep building and shifting their sand dunes. Mountain gales keep sweeping rock waste off the slopes and summits, and sowing it down in the valleys.

Only a very strong wind can blow pebbles, but the dust particles carried by ordinary winds can add up enormously. In most places, there is some wind blowing most of the time, and there is an ocean of air miles thick to hold the dust.

During the past generation, farmers in the midwestern United States have seen sad proof of the power of moving air. In periods of drought, winds sweeping across the dusty fields have stolen thousands of tons of valuable soil. In March 1936, the skies over New York City were half-darkened by soil blowing in from the so-called Dust Bowl of the south-central states, 1,300 miles away. In a few years, the land level in some areas of the Dust Bowl was lowered by three to four feet.

Summer visitors in Cape Cod, reading its history, are surprised to learn that when first settled by the white man in the seventeenth century it was heavily forested, with rich virgin soil. As farmers cleared the land, the winds began blowing away the topsoil, and by the mid-1800's most of this was gone. The winds kept blowing, and the Cape's harbors, much needed by the fishermen and whalers, were filling up. Only strenuous efforts by the Cape Codders, including widespread planting of tough beach grass and young trees, saved their homeland from becoming a desert.

In southern Wyoming and certain other desert areas of the West, the wind over long periods has lowered the land level by 150 feet. Parts of the Libyan Desert, in Africa, have been cut to a depth of 420 feet below the level of the nearby Mediterranean Sea.

WIND AND SAND

In deserts and along open beaches, the wind is free and strong as a shaper of the land. Blowing almost constantly, the wind keeps sandblasting the high places. If there is much loose sand, the wind may keep busy at the task of piling it up into dunes and then scattering it again.

Dunes have many forms, depending on wind direction, wind strength, and the kind of material being blown. Many are crescent-shaped.

Symbol of Dust Bowl—*This farm, in Morton County, Kansas, was one of thousands ruined by drought and wind in dry period of 1930's. Wind carried some Dust Bowl soils as far as Atlantic Ocean.*

Wind work on desert—*Among forms taken by sand dunes, crescent is common. Arrows indicate air movements.*

Usually a dune has a gentle slope on the side against which the wind is blowing—the windward side. As the wind rides up this slope, it loses speed and has to drop some of the material it is carrying. This falls on the other side of the dune, the lee side, and piles up to form a sharper slope there.

The higher the dune grows, the more it slows down the wind blowing against it. The more the wind slows down, the more sand it will drop on the lee side of the dune. Once a dune is started, therefore, it may grow very large. But then a really powerful wind may come along, and when the sand has settled we find the old dune gone, and maybe a new one nearby.

Anchored dunes—*Yellow lupine, covering sand dunes on Oregon shore, helps to hold them for a season.*

Dunes can be compared to snowdrifts, but they may build much higher. In the American deserts, dunes rise to heights of 300 feet. In the Sahara there are dunes 600 to 700 feet high.

In any region, the wind blows more from one direction than from others. Therefore, it tends to move the sand or soil mostly in one direction. Entering a region from one side, the wind works to sweep up all the loose material on that side and move it over to the other side.

Traveling dunes sometimes become a menace to man. Many a cottage along a seashore has been covered by a marching dune. The same thing has happened to farms and ranches in desert and drought-ridden areas.

GLACIAL DUST

In certain areas toward which the prevailing winds blow, geologists often notice deposits of a kind called loess. This consists of extremely tiny rock particles—so tiny that even when blown about by the wind, they cannot hit and rub against one another hard enough to wear off their sharp, ragged edges. The edges tend to become interlocked with one another as the particles are deposited. So,

when we find loess exposed in road cuts and trenches, it may be very firm, standing up in cliffs 30 to 40 feet high. Often it is cracked and jointed like rock.

Deposits of loess as much as 40 feet deep are found in the Mississippi Valley. Much of this material was probably rubbed off our western mountains during the glacial ages, then blown eastward.

The world's greatest deposits of loess are in China. Here they reach depths of several hundred feet. Probably the origin of this dust is the Gobi Desert, in the interior of Asia.

WAVE WORK

Ever chewing away at the land's edges is the sea. Waves, currents, and dissolving power are its teeth. Only occasional shifting of the crust, causing blocks of land to rise, has prevented the sea from chewing away the dry lands completely.

Ordinary ocean waves are caused by wind. A wind blowing at 30 miles an hour across a wide area of ocean for one day can make waves 15 feet high and 300 feet long. Even after traveling 2,000 miles, these waves will be 2½ feet high. Waves do travel thousands of miles, and so, even when there

Erosion on seacoasts—*Coast that is advancing against sea (left) is likely to have gently sloping shore, with series of abandoned beaches appearing as terraces at higher levels. Coast that is retreating before ocean (right) often has cliffs and outlying shore-remnants called stacks.*

ADVANCING SHORELINE

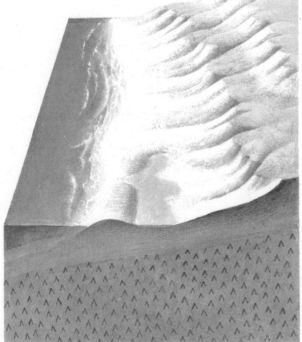

RETREATING SHORELINE

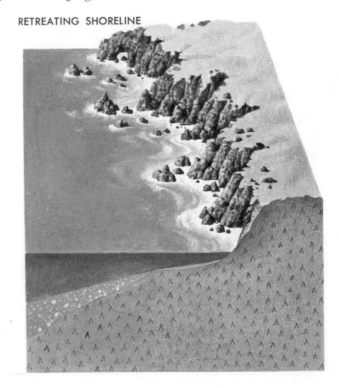

is no wind blowing against a coast, waves keep pushing and swirling in.

As a wave nears the shore, its under part is slowed down by friction with the bottom. The top of the wave keeps going, curls forward, and breaks. A lot of the energy that has been carrying the wave along is in the top as it spills forward.

As every swimmer knows, a breaking ocean wave has great pushing power. It can knock off large chunks of a soft cliff. Then, as it retreats, its sucking power can pull more chunks out of the cliff. The bottom of the cliff is dug out, and the upper parts overhang and fall. And so the cliff is chopped away little by little.

As a wave slides back, it carries with it sand and rock taken from the shore. This material is caught by the next wave and carried shoreward again. As the process goes on and on, the material becomes sorted according to size. Larger pieces of stone are dropped near shore, and smaller ones farther out. The constant rubbing and knocking of all these fragments against one another smooths and rounds them. The grains knocked off them form beach sand.

Running seaward from a beach there is usually an underwater platform, or terrace, of sand and gravel. This is material that the waves "work with." The platform slopes gradually out until it reaches the depth at which the force of the waves is not felt. This depth is often about thirty feet, but varies. Beyond the platform the real ocean bottom begins.

Wherever waves are working against soft material, the retreat of the shore may be rapid. The east shore of Cape Cod, for example, is retreating at the rate of about a foot per year—in relatively calm years. In the hurricane of September 1944, the raging ocean cut away some parts of the sandy cliffs to a depth of fifty feet.

Even a rocky shore cannot win against the waves. They scrape and pound the rocks with

sand and pebbles. They hurl driftwood and other refuse against the rocks. Water forced into cracks in rocks by the power of waves wedges rocks apart, just as frost does. And so a rocky cliff, in the end, can be destroyed as completely as a sandy or clayey one.

Work of currents—*Shoals at west end of Nantucket Island, Mass., are seen through water from the air.*

mostly by the action of waves, wind, and tides. The ways in which they work depend on the shape of the coastline and the depths of the water there. Some shorelines, such as those of Long Island, are being constantly reshaped by the work of the currents.

Currents running along shore pick up eroded material, carry it for a time, and drop it to form sandbars, spits, and even islands. Thousands of tons of sand and clay torn from the Cape Cod cliffs each year are picked up by currents and dropped on the bars at the northern and southern corners of the Cape, many miles away. Like processes are going on, day after day, along shores all over the world.

In time an uneven shore tends to get straightened out by the action of waves and currents. The land that sticks out into the ocean is the land that gets hit hardest by the waves. At the same time, many bays tend to fill gradually with sand brought in by tides and currents that drop the sand as they lose speed.

It is along rocky coasts that the waves have done some of their most beautiful sculpturing. The Gaspé Peninsula, the coast of Maine, and the shores of northern California, Oregon, and Washington offer some of the best examples. England and France, too, have spectacular rocky shores. Out of the hard cliffs along these coasts the waves have carved caves, towers, and other such forms.

The sea may cut fast into a sinking shore, slicing it up into isolated blocks called stacks. Beaches may be steep, narrow, or non-existent. Elsewhere, rock debris or current-borne sand may be building a shore outward. Inland, near the shore, one may see a series of abandoned beaches in the form of terraces.

CURRENTS SHALLOW AND DEEP

Close allies of the waves in their war against the land are the shore currents. These are caused

Wave breakthrough—*Flowerlike pattern of coastal sands, seen on bottom from air, was created when hurricane-driven waves broke through sandbar at Moriches Inlet, Fire Island, New York.*

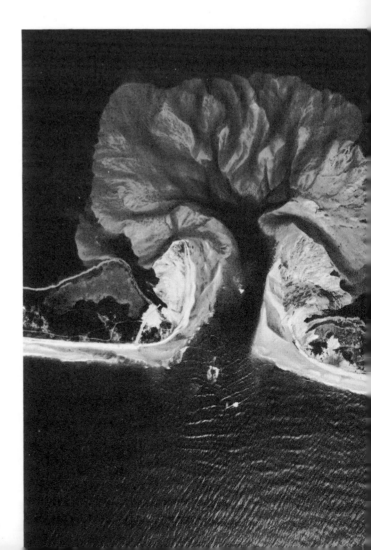

62

Vanishing coastline—*In vicinity of Lizard Head, on coast of England, sea is advancing and waves are cutting shore away, section by section. Note numerous stacks. Compare with California shore, page 19.*

Even undersea currents join in the task of cutting away Earth's crust. These are generally quite lazy; most move at four to five miles an hour or less. But even at such speeds they can shift large amounts of sand and other sediments.

Oceanographers have reported bottom currents in the Atlantic that move at speeds of 60 miles per hour. As cold water at the ocean's surface "falls" thousands of feet toward the bottom, it forms currents of gigantic power. Such currents have carved ravines and gorges in the continental shelves and submarine mountain ranges, and possibly have cut some of the deep valleys in the ocean floors.

Two types of seashores—*Map shows part of southern Connecticut (above) and northern Long Island (below). Rising sea has invaded Connecticut river valleys and made islands of high areas formerly part of mainland. Waves and currents have molded soft, sandy shores of Long Island into complex systems of spits, bars, and bays.*

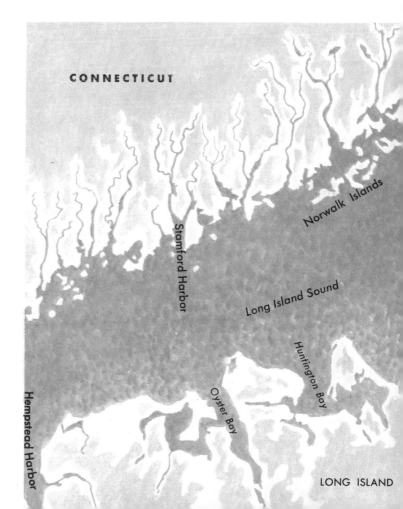

CONNECTICUT

Stamford Harbor

Norwalk Islands

Long Island Sound

Huntington Bay

Oyster Bay

Hempstead Harbor

LONG ISLAND

Water-carved underworld—*Fantastic displays of stalactites and stalagmites in caverns of Luray, Virginia, testify to dissolving power of ground water. Caverns and systems of tunnels are typical of limestone regions.*

Ground Water

Most of us have at some time watched the drilling of a well. A pointed pipe is driven down through soil and rock, little by little. Sooner or later, at a depth of twenty feet, or fifty, or maybe one hundred feet or deeper, the drillers strike water. The bottom end of the pipe reaches a place underground where the soil or rock is saturated with water, like a sponge.

Every driller knows that he could strike water almost anywhere on Earth—even in the middle of the Sahara Desert—if he drilled deep enough. Our planet's crust is more or less soaked with water, not only where we see oceans and lakes and rivers, but beneath what we call dry land. The water occupies cracks and tiny spaces between the grains of soil and rock. In some regions such spaces add up to a great deal of room for underground water; in others, there is little space. But

wherever there is "dry" land, we can be fairly sure that there is water somewhere beneath its surface. Geologists call it ground water, and it is very important in the story of Earth's crust.

WHERE FROM?

The origin of ground water was one of those geological problems that puzzled the ancients. They guessed that most of the water seen in and on the crust comes up from deep reservoirs.

Today we know that only a little of the total supply of ground water is produced within Earth's crust. Such water, called "juvenile" by geologists, originates from chemical processes. Leonardo da Vinci, who had much practical experience in the draining of swamps, was the first to grasp the idea that the water which falls as rain and feeds rivers also may seep underground

64

Where water comes from—*Artist's drawing in 17th-century book* Cataractae Mundi *("Rivers of the World") attempts to explain origin of water. Neptune, God of Sea, pours water into monster, which then spouts it high and far over land and sea.*

and form rivers and reservoirs there. With Aristotle's understanding that water is "raised" from the oceans by the Sun and falls on the mountains to feed rivers, Leonardo's idea completes our modern picture of the water cycle, by which the power of the Sun has kept the lands watered through the ages.

WHERE THE RAIN GOES

Earth's atmosphere, heated by the Sun, is constantly evaporating enormous amounts of water from both the oceans and the land. Sooner or later this moisture falls as rain or snow. The amount that falls each year would be enough to cover our globe with water to an average depth of 3½ feet.

Arid regions get only a few inches of that water annually. Regions of average rainfall, such as the eastern United States, get about 40 inches.

In parts of India and some other areas, the rainfall is 30 to 40 feet.

The water runs down slopes, collects in lakes, works its way underground. It is used by plants and animals; it flows into rivers. Much of it is soon evaporated into the air, but part of this soon falls again as rain or snow. Eventually, about a fourth of all the molecules of moisture that fall as rain or snow reach the sea.

It may take a million years for any particular molecule of water to get from the sea to the land and back to the sea again. After falling from a cloud, it may be in a river for a time, then underground, later in a lake or swamp, then up in the atmosphere, now in the body of an animal, and again in a river. There is a good chance that much of its time will be spent within the Earth's crust as ground water.

Water that falls on soil, or runs onto it, works down between the soil grains. If the grains are

Ancient art of dowsing—*Illustration from 17th-century book shows how location of water was believed to be indicated by magical behavior of forked stick in hands of dowser. Smoke suggests occult art.*

65

large, as sand grains usually are, it will work down fairly fast. If the grains are small, as clay particles are, the downward movement will be slower.

Gravity keeps pulling at the water. Yet some moisture sticks to the soil grains. (That is why soil may remain damp for many days after a rain.) The smaller the grains, the better they can hold onto the water. The downward flow of water through small grains is slow.

Some regions get little rain. There will be seasons when the soil dries out to depth of several feet. But, rain or shine, there is always water somewhere below.

As water moves down, sooner or later it comes to bedrock. If this rock has many tiny connecting channels between the rock grains, the water will percolate, or "leak," through it. The water will also run down through any joints it finds. Joints are cracks that cut across layers of bedrock.

But downward-moving water will meet, somewhere, a layer of rock or clay through which it cannot pass. The water will travel along this waterproof layer until it does find a kind of material that will let it get through.

Underground water is thus constantly in motion, zigzagging its way deeper and deeper until it reaches the level where all the available cracks and crannies are already full. That level is called the water table.

THE WATER TABLE

Take a glass and half-fill it with sand. Now put in a few tablespoons of water. The water will sink to the bottom, filling the space between the grains of sand up to a certain level—the water table.

The sand in the glass is like Earth's crust. If you dig down far enough, you will reach water.

In the glass of sand, the water table is quite flat and level, and motionless. But that is not so underground. Layers of bedrock usually have bumps and hollows, and they slant. So under-

ground water that collects or flows on these layers also has an uneven surface. Its shape depends on the nature of the rock formations above and below it. Also, the water is usually in motion here, because more water keeps coming down and leveling out as it reaches the table.

All the movements of ground water are determined by the nature of the rock strata. Shales are likely to be close-grained and lacking in joints, so that water can hardly get through. Sandstone usually has more space available between the grains, and more joints. Limestone strata often have many tunnels made by percolating water. Dense rocks, such as granite and basalt, afford little space between grains but may be cracked enough to let water get through easily.

We hear of "underground reservoirs," but it would be inaccurate to think of these as great caverns and tunnels full of water. Such cavities can exist only near the ground surface, where the pressure of overlying rock is not great. Wells that get water from depths of many hundreds of feet are getting it from networks of small spaces. Beyond 2,000 or 3,000 feet the pressure is too

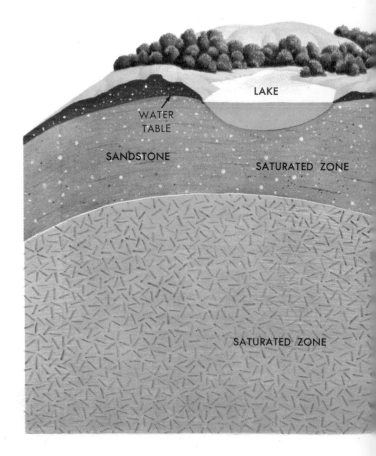

Ground water—Where water table is at land surface, it forms lake, spring, brook, swamp. Below it, all permeable rock contains water. Well at left gets water from porous sandstone. At far right, shale yielded little water; so well was driven down to porous limestone. Falling water table made middle well go dry.

great for much space to exist even in fine networks. A very small quantity of ground water may, however, penetrate to depths of miles.

WELLS SHALLOW AND DEEP

An old-fashioned well is simply a hole dug down below the water table, with the inside walled up to prevent caving in. For a modern "driven" well, a pipe with a perforated point is driven down. At the top of this pipe is a pump to raise the water. Driving a well is like sticking a soda straw down into our glass of water and sand.

Because of differences in rock structures, there is more water underground in some places than in others. Before driving a well, therefore, experts try to find what the rock structures are.

Ground water usually has minerals dissolved in it. Bicarbonate of calcium or magnesium, especially, makes water "hard." A lot of soap is required to make suds in it. "Soft" water contains few such minerals. In some desert regions, the water contains minerals that make it undrinkable.

Water supply near the surface may be very limited, or may become polluted by sewage or waste from factories. For a bigger or purer supply, a well may be driven very deep.

Artesian wells were named from the region of Artois, in France, where the first such wells in Europe were drilled. A true artesian well may go very deep, yet does not need a pump to bring the water up. The bottom of the well pipe is in a flow of water moving down between long slanting rock layers from a place higher than the top of the well. The weight of the water pushing down the rock layer is greater than the weight of water in the pipe; so the water rises in the pipe.

WATER SHORTAGES

In dry seasons, the water table gradually falls. Where it falls below the bottom of a well, that well goes dry.

In some areas, such as parts of the southwestern United States, wells are pumping water out of the ground faster than rain is replacing it. Water tables are falling, farms are drying up, and drinking water has been sold by the gallon.

Sometimes the sinking of a water table causes rock and soil above it to cave in. Parts of Mexico

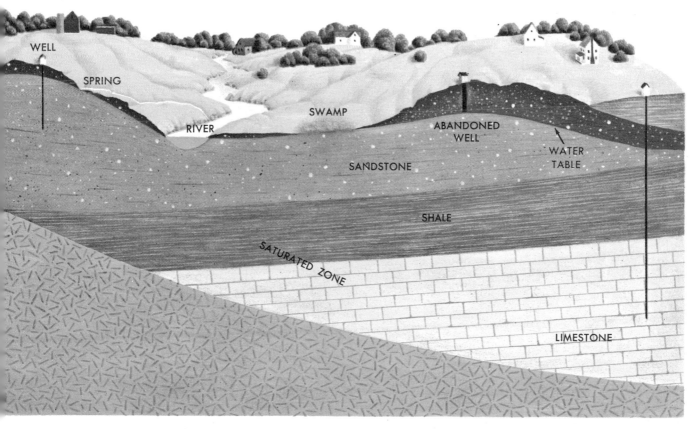

CAVERNS AND SINKS

Limestone caverns show what ground water can do in its age-long task of dissolving rock underground. Take Mammoth Cave, in Kentucky, as an example.

Some 225 to 275 million years ago, an arm of the Gulf of Mexico gradually reached up through what is now the central United States. For perhaps 30 million years it stayed there. Then the land rose and the sea retreated, leaving a deposit of limestone covering thousands of square miles. This rock, as much as 1,200 feet thick in Kentucky, had formed from minerals in the sea water and from the limy remains of untold trillions of tiny sea plants and animals.

The water table remained high for a long time. Through cracks and crannies within the limestone, water kept flowing. Oxygen and carbon dioxide, picked up by the water from air and from plants, helped the water to dissolve the mineral calcium carbonate out of the limestone. (Limestone *is* mainly calcium carbonate.) Slowly the water made larger and larger channels, and some of these eventually became large caverns. Roofs of caverns far down collapsed, because of the weight of the overlying rock, but caverns nearer the surface remained intact.

Mammoth Cave is one of the largest networks of these channels and caverns so far discovered.

City are sinking a foot or two per year. Walls of buildings have cracked, streets have buckled, water and gas mains have broken.

Wherever man uses water faster than nature supplies it, the water table becomes a problem. Keeping up the water supply for modern civilization is a challenge to science.

How an artesian well works—*Water entering at upper left travels down between shale strata. Water spouts out of well pipe (lower right) because top of pipe is lower than source of water. Inset shows principle.*

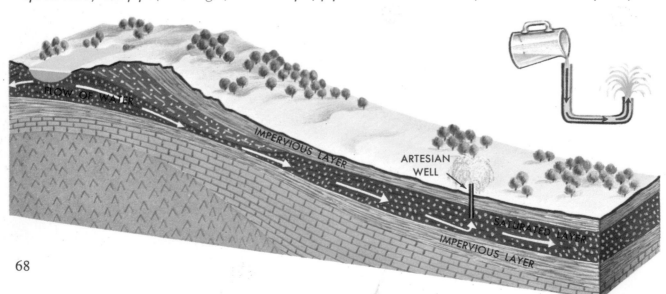

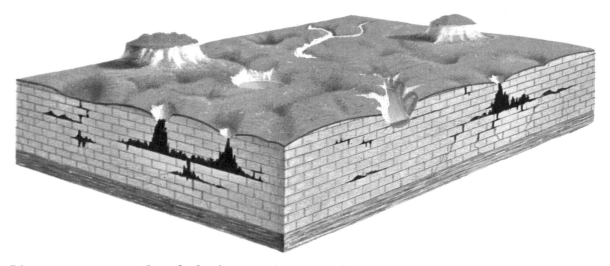

Limestone country—*Where bedrocks are of limestone, dissolving power of water creates a region of sinkholes, caverns, and underground streams. Surface features of region are called karst topography.*

Today, because the water table has fallen, we can explore the upper channels. Those farther down are still under water.

Above the water table, stalactites and stalagmites have formed. In a process that may take thousands of years for the big ones, they are built by water dripping from cave ceilings.

Some stalactites grow in an interesting tubular form. Evaporation of some of the water before it falls leaves a gradually growing deposit of calcium carbonate, in the form of a ring around the point from which the water is dripping. As more and more mineral is deposited, the ring gets longer and longer, becoming a tube through which the water keeps trickling down. This tube is the stalactite. It may keep growing for hundreds or thousands of years as water keeps coming down through the channel inside and as other mineral-bearing water from the ceiling spreads downward and evaporates on the outside.

Stalagmites are formed by water that falls to the cave floor. Here calcium carbonate builds upward in piles that suggest "reverse" stalactites. Where a stalactite and a stalagmite meet, a column or pillar is formed.

Ground water has been dissolving away the thick limestone of this region at the rate of a foot of elevation each 2,000 years. Beneath the land

Water work—*"Gothic Palace" in Lehman Caves, Snake Mountains, near Ely, Nevada, is favorite tourist spot. In some limestone regions, thousands of miles of water-made tunnels invite "spelunkers."*

surface are millions of miles of channels, large and small. The countryside is dotted with "sinks," which are hollows that show where roofs of caves have collapsed. There are many "lost" rivers, also —rivers that disappear into underground channels.

The modern sport of "spelunking," or exploring caverns, has become highly popular in certain limestone regions. Systems of water-made tunnels, some of them miles long, are a challenge to the ingenious and the daring. Water-filled channels are sometimes explored by swimmers with artificial breathing devices. Spelunking is safe only in groups with experienced leaders.

Lakes and Swamps

Lakes are among the pleasantest gifts of nature to man. They are usually beautiful to look at, interesting to fish in, cool to swim in, and breezy to sail on. They are homes for birds, fish, and other animals. They supply us with water. They give us a feeling of space in a crowded world. It is a pity that lakes are so rare in most regions and that, geologically speaking, they are so short-lived.

Areas where lakes are common, especially northern Europe and northern North America, often are areas that were covered with ice sheets in recent geologic times—meaning during the past 100,000 years or so. Lakes occur elsewhere, as in Africa and South America, but in smaller num-

bers. France, Spain, and non-mountainous countries of southern Europe have few lakes. The truth is that processes in Earth's crust do not often work to form lakes and, as we shall see, they tend to destroy lakes that do exist.

HOW LAKES COME TO BE

Essentially, a lake is a body of water lying in a basin, or hollow, whose bottom is below the water table. Water finds its way into this basin by way of direct rainfall, streams, or springs. Most lakes receive more water than they need to stay full, and the excess flows out through the lowest outlet it can find at the edge.

Land of lakes—*Christian River area, Alaska, is typical of regions where ice sheets gouged basins in bedrocks and made thousands of lakes possible. Down-cutting by outlet streams will eventually drain the lakes.*

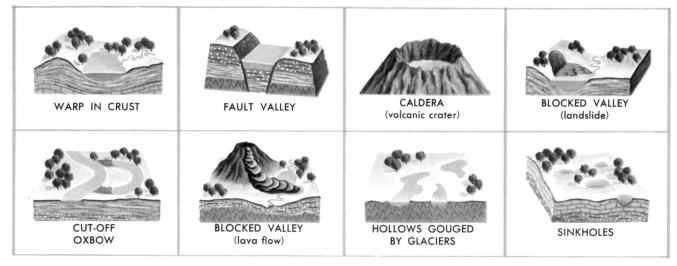

Eight Kinds of Lake Basins

WARP IN CRUST

FAULT VALLEY

CALDERA
(volcanic crater)

BLOCKED VALLEY
(landslide)

CUT-OFF
OXBOW

BLOCKED VALLEY
(lava flow)

HOLLOWS GOUGED
BY GLACIERS

SINKHOLES

Everyone has heard of "bottomless" lakes, but of course no such lakes exist. Every lake will be found to have a bottom—if your sounding line is long enough.

The famous lakes and lake regions of the world illustrate, in their different ways, how lake basins may be formed by nature.

Beautiful Lake Cristobal, near Lake City, Colorado, shows how a lake can result from the damming of a river valley. This lake formed after the river valley was blocked by the famous "Slumgullion" earthflow—an enormous mass of moist volcanic ash moving down from the nearby hills.

From the country of Israel, east of the Mediterranean Sea, to Northern Rhodesia, in southern Africa, runs an irregular 3,500-mile chain of valleys. These were formed by a great rift in the Earth's crust, and some are now filled with water. One holds the waters of the famous Dead Sea, between Israel and Jordan. The Sea of Galilee and the Red Sea lie in other valleys of the chain. Farther south the rift valleys are filled by Lakes Tanganyika and Nyasa.

Rift-valley lakes include the deepest in the world. Lake Tanganyika has depths down to 4,700 feet—nearly a mile. Lake Baikal, in southeastern Siberia, is 5,710 feet deep—more than a mile; it is the deepest lake in the world, with its bottom 4,226 feet below sea level. This body of water contains something like 5,800 cubic miles—almost as much as all the Great Lakes. A famous rift-valley lake in North America is Lake Tahoe (Bigler Lake), on the border of California and Nevada; it is over 1,600 feet deep.

Here and there we find old volcanic craters full of water. Crater Lake, in Oregon, is one of the most famous of these lakes. Cooling lava sealed the bottom of the crater of an extinct volcano—Mount Mazama—so that it could contain water.

In areas where the bedrocks are of limestone, such as Kentucky, lakes occupy some of the sinks. The sinks were formed by the collapse of the roofs of caverns. The lake level is the level of the water table at that place.

Among the most scenic lakes are those that lie at the feet of glaciers. The basins may be hollows scooped out by the moving ice, or valleys dammed by rock waste. These lakes are fed by melting ice.

Even in some hilly or mountainous regions from which the glaciers have long since vanished, such as the Adirondacks of New York state, some of these glacial lakes still exist. Now they are fed directly by rainfall and ground water.

The northern areas of North America and Europe are dotted with lakes which occupy basins that were scraped and gouged out of the land surface by ice sheets of past glacial ages. These ice sheets were not mountain glaciers of the sort we see in the Alps today. They were like great seas of ice, thousands of feet thick, creeping down from the north and covering thousands upon thousands of square miles. The Scandinavian lands of Europe, and such areas as Minnesota and Maine in

71

their location. How some of these small lakes were formed makes an interesting geological story, and also explains how glacial lakes formed in many other areas also.

During the glacial ages, an edge of the great ice sheet spreading down from the north was about at the present location of Cape Cod. Several times, apparently, the climate grew a little warmer and the front of the ice sheet melted back; then the climate got cooler and the ice sheet pushed forward again.

During melting times, great blocks of ice fell off the front of the ice sheet. When the front came forward again, it would ride up over some of the blocks and grind them with stupendous force down into the sand and clay beneath. When the front retreated again, many blocks were left buried deep in the ground.

Eventually, in warmer times, the buried blocks melted, leaving big holes in the land. Many of these holes today reach down below the level of the water table and so are filled with fresh water.

THE GREAT LAKES

Most famous of all the North American bodies of water created by the ice sheets are the Great Lakes. These occupy five ancient river valleys. The valleys are millions of years old, but the lakes

the United States, can thank the grinding ice of long ago for hundreds of their beautiful lakes.

Cape Cod, an arm of Massachusetts running out into the Atlantic Ocean, is a heap of sand and clay left by melting ice of the recent glacial ages. Dotting the Cape are many fresh-water ponds—rather unexpected, you might think, considering

Great Lakes—11,000 B.C.—*Ice sheet covers most of present area. Lakes drain west through Mississippi and east through Mohawk and Hudson river valleys.*

9,000 B.C.—*Mohawk Valley is now blocked with ice. Drainage therefore occurs southwestward from old Lake Michigan basin to Mississippi Valley.*

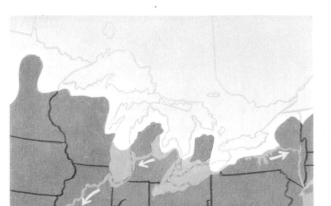

The river that became a lake—Deep Lake, in Sun Lakes State Park, eastern Washington, occupies part of former river valley in lava landscape. Note potholes gouged out long ago by whirlpools of river.

are much younger. They were born during the most recent of the glacial ages.

That age was closing 8,000 to 10,000 years ago. The ice sheets that had reached far down into North America had melted back to near the present northern border of the United States. As the ice retreated, the old river valleys, gouged deeper than ever by the ice, reappeared, and meltwaters from the ice filled them.

Blocked in the north by ice, the overflow waters turned southward. For varying periods they found their way to the Mississippi or, shifting in the opposite direction, drained out by way of the Mohawk River, which runs eastward to feed the Hudson.

The ice sheet kept melting. Its southern edges moved farther and farther back into Canada. Land that had been under the mile-thick ice gradually rose as the weight was removed. A new route for the overflow waters opened in Canada—it was the St. Lawrence River. And so was completed the chain by which waters today travel eastward from Lakes Superior and Michigan, through Lakes Huron, Erie, and Ontario, and finally through the St. Lawrence to the sea.

The water left in the Great Lakes by the glaciers evaporated and drained away long ago. But in this region there is plenty of rain, and the lakes receive drainage from surrounding lands with twice the area that the lakes alone have. The lakes hold about 6,000 cubic miles of water—enough to fill a space 20 miles wide, 50 miles long, and 6 miles high. The lakes are so well supplied with water that they pour 1½ to 2 million gallons into the St. Lawrence every second.

7,000 B.C.—Retreat of ice allows drainage westward through Lake Superior and eastward once more through the Mohawk and Hudson river valleys.

6,000 B.C.—Further retreat of ice sheet and rising of land to south of it allow northeastward drainage (as today) through St. Lawrence Valley.

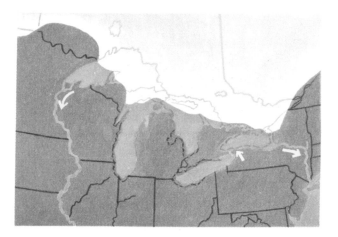

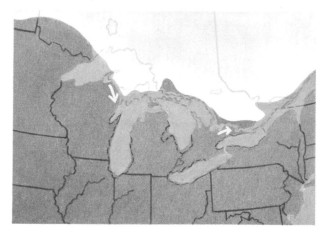

73

Where ice blocks melted—*Massachusetts has many cranberry bogs and lakes like these near Monponsett. Basins are relics of recent ice ages. Ground sank to form basins as buried ice blocks melted.*

The most dangerous threat to the average lake is its own outlet. Water running through the outlet cuts it deeper and deeper, and so the lake loses water faster and faster. Eventually the lake may become just a wide hollow with a stream.

Some of these processes are already going on in the Great Lakes and may, eventually, cause the lakes to vanish.

For one thing, all the lakes are gradually filling with sediments. Lake Michigan is filling at the rate of three inches every hundred years—fast enough to become filled in 250,000 years.

If the climate should become drier and the water level should fall, the 250,000 years might be cut in half. All the lakes face this danger.

But there is still another threat. As visitors to Niagara Falls learn, the gorge being cut by the Niagara River is advancing toward Lake Erie at the rate of four to five feet per year. In about 25,000 years, the gorge should reach Lake Erie, and the lake will be emptied. Very likely the flow of water all along the chain of lakes will speed up, the connections between the lakes will be deepened, and the lakes will be converted into river valleys—as they were before the glaciers came.

The truth is that in modern times more lakes are vanishing than are being formed. Since the last

WHY LAKES DISAPPEAR

Lakes are born by geological accidents. Likewise, the life of a lake may be ended by an accident. If the climate becomes a little drier, evaporation may take water out of the lake faster than water flows in. A lake may fill with sediments washed or blown into it, or with the remains of plants and animals that have lived in it. A gradual warping of the land may eliminate the basin.

How Niagara Gorge may some day empty Lake Erie

| **Today**—*Gorge reaches only to Niagara Falls.* | **15,000 years from now** — *Gorge is halfway to Buffalo.* | **25,000 years from now**— *Gorge empties Lake Erie.* |

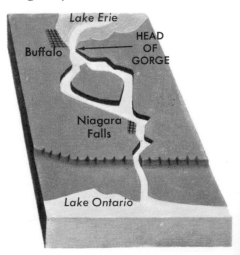

Making most of a salt lake—Workers in Colombia, South America, rake up salt for industrial use. Such lakes afford common salt and, in some cases, other minerals such as borax, gypsum, and potash.

glacial period, giant bodies of water such as Lake Bonneville, in Utah, and Lake Agassiz, in Canada, have shrunk to ghosts of their former selves. Even the Great Lakes were once larger than they are now. Within the short span of human history, Lake Ngami in Africa has dwindled from an inland sea to a marsh. By their very nature, the so-called salt lakes—which make up 40 per cent of all—are "dying."

Among the new lakes forming in our time are those which, like Lake Pontchartrain in Louisiana, are created by the formation of sandbars along seacoasts and deltas.

GREAT SALT LAKE'S ANCESTOR

Old Lake Bonneville is an example of how an enormous lake—practically an inland ocean—can fade away because of a change in climate.

In glacial times, this lake occupied the western half of what is now Utah, and was as much as 1,000 feet deep. In those days, the climate of Utah was wetter, and streams were feeding the lake

Dwindling giant—*Lake Bonneville, vast and deep during last ice ages, has shrunk to become Great Salt Lake of our time. Map shows shrinkage.*

more water than it lost by evaporation and by drainage through its outlets. But the climate gradually became dryer. The lake's level began to fall, and its area to shrink. Eventually the water level fell below the level of the outlets, so that no more water was lost through them. Shrinkage of the lake's area also reduced the rate of water loss by

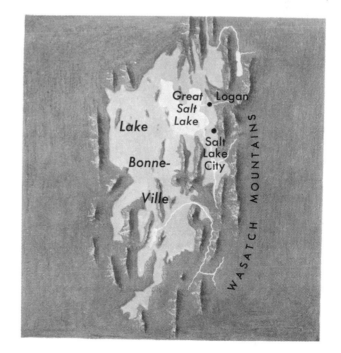

75

evaporation. Thus, at last, a balance was reached, and the lake ceased to shrink except for the seasonal changes.

Today, shrunken Lake Bonneville is known as Great Salt Lake. Its area is only a third of the area of the Lake Bonneville of glacial times, and its average depth is only 12 feet. Around it are vast stretches of dry salt flats. On the sides of the mountains that rise near the lake are traces of ancient shorelines as much as 1,000 feet above the present water level. This present lake has no outlet; it needs every drop of water that comes by rainfall and by streams. If the climate becomes slightly dryer, the lake may dwindle away to nothing.

FRESH WATER AND SALT

Lake Bonneville in glacial times contained fresh water. But Great Salt Lake today is saltier than sea water. Why?

In glacial times, Lake Bonneville was receiving lots of rainwater and meltwater. This was enough to keep the lake fresh despite the salt being brought in by rivers from the rather salty nearby hills. But in time, as the glaciers melted away and the climate became dryer, the supply of pure water dwindled. The level of the lake sank below the outlets. Evaporation kept taking water out of the lake without taking the salt, which was no longer escaping through the outlet. And so the lake became saltier and saltier.

Lake Bonneville's story is not unusual. The remains of old shorelines and basins of at least seventy-five salt lakes have been counted in the dry region west of the Rockies between Oregon and New Mexico. Salt lakes have been common also in North Africa, Asia Minor, and central Asia. The largest salt lakes now in existence are the Caspian Sea and the Dead Sea.

Glacial relic—*Lower Ausable Lake, in New York's Adirondacks, lies in valley carved by glaciers during recent ice ages. Adirondacks are rich in glacier-made lake basins.*

High water table—*Level of water table determines whether area will be lake, swamp, or dry land. Table is barely at surface here, near Lake Charles, Louisiana, and cypress swamp has formed.*

SWAMPS AND MARSHES

Where the water table barely reaches the ground surface, a swamp may form. A little dry weather may cause the water table to fall enough for the swamp to dry up. One heavy rain may raise the water table enough to make the swamp a shallow lake.

Some regions have vast swampy areas. In the lower Mississippi Valley, for example, there is a tremendous volume of water moving barely below the surface. It keeps thousands of square miles of land in a swampy condition most of the year.

Among the most famous swamps of North America are the Everglades of Florida and the Dismal Swamp of North Carolina and Virginia.

These are lowlands that were covered, until a few thousand years ago, by the ocean. As the land rose, the salt water drained away and fresh water took its place. The swamps may vanish if the land rises a little more. Or, if the land sinks a little, the sea will again move in. If the land sinks just enough so that tides can bring in salt water, the swamps will be salt marshes.

Swamps often are fine refuges for wildlife. When drained, they can make highly fertile land for farms, or conveniently located land for factories, docks, and residential developments. Draining is done by digging trenches. Placed properly, these lower the water table in just the spots where dry land is wanted.

The Ways of Rivers

To the heat of the Sun we owe not only our weather but also, oddly enough, our rivers. Thanks to the Sun, sea water becomes clouds, which become rain, which becomes water on and in the ground. A river is a long, inclined trench that is kept filled by ground water and, to some extent, directly by rainwater.

Water easily takes any shape we give it. Yet, powered by gravity, it represents one of the greatest agents at work on our planet. Ground water at the surface is freer to move than water percolating through crannies underground; it is freer to push and pluck, and to carry rock debris along with it. Seeking its way back to the oceans, it wears down mountains, carves canyons, fills valleys with sediments. It is in the form of rivers, mainly, that water shapes our landscapes.

River waters of the United States alone carry and push something like 800 million tons of debris into the oceans each year. Even more than that is picked up by rivers, carried for a time, and then dropped again on the land.

In a human lifetime, erosion makes little difference in the landscapes we know. It is hard to imagine anything so slow as the wearing down of a mountain range, for example, or the cutting of a canyon. Yet geologists say that erosion, which is mainly the work of rivers, could have worn down the continents to sea level not once but several times since the planet formed. The continents of today are above water only because underground forces have kept pushing them up while erosion has been planing them down.

RIVER SECRETS

Like mountains and valleys, rivers were taken for granted by man until modern times. Most rivers, it seemed, had been created along with everything else; they had existed as long as the world. Just a few odd ones, within the memory of man, had mysteriously appeared or as mysteriously vanished.

To the ancients and the learned men of the Middle Ages, a river was simply water running *over* the land, following whatever valleys happened to be handy as channels. Scholars discussed where the water came from, but if anyone ever carefully traced a river back to its sources to find out, he

has been forgotten. Although Aristotle had said that rain and snow feed rivers in the mountains, as late as the seventeenth century the prevailing idea about the origin of rivers was the one offered by the German scholar-priest Athanasius Kircher. Water starts in the hills, explained Kircher; it fol-

Exuberance of youth—*Among best-known North American rivers is Yellowstone, whose swift, churning waters have cut through soft red and yellow rock strata to form zigzagging valley in Yellowstone National Park. Swift, twisting stream with its waterfalls is in what geologists call "youthful" phase.*

Among the most famous of the river geologists was an American, Major John Wesley Powell, U.S.A. Despite the loss of an arm in the Civil War, this all-around naturalist led several expeditions to explore the Rocky Mountain region. His greatest exploit was the river trip down the Colorado River from southern Wyoming to the western end of the Grand Canyon in Arizona. Baked by the sun, stung by wind-blown sand, tossed by rough water, forced to portage again and again by menacing rapids and falls, handicapped by losses of supplies and instruments, Powell and his nine companions nevertheless found ways to study the ever-changing behavior of the river and the channels it had carved through the ages. It was the greatest opportunity ever to observe a river under all sorts of conditions —flowing narrow and wide, deep and shallow, fast and slow, through plain and canyon, soft rock and hard. In going through the Grand Canyon, moreover, Powell was able to follow and map the most splendid display of sedimentary rocks on the continent—embodying a billion years of Earth history.

RIVER BEGINNINGS

Imagine a small, rocky hill in Pennsylvania. Throughout the year, rain falls on this hill about twice a week. Some raindrops striking the hill are quickly captured by plant roots, and some soon evaporate into the air again. Many run together to form little rills, which run into gullies, and these lead into a brook that flows down into the valley.

Many drops work down through cracks in the bedrock, and there join water from earlier rains in cracks and crannies. This water inside the hill is in motion. It keeps finding its way down, ever down. Some comes out of the hillside at a lower point in the form of a spring. This spring and others feed the brook leading down into the valley. Even when there has been no rain for days or weeks, the springs may keep producing.

Down in the valley, the brook joins another brook from a neighboring hill. After running a half mile, the waters of the two brooks are joined

lows valleys down to the land, finds the sea, leaks through the ocean bottom, and somehow finds its way underground back into the hills to start its journey over again.

In those days, digging wells gave men some knowledge about underground water, but this knowledge was entangled with superstitions and large amounts of pure imagination. It did not help much in explaining rivers.

No one had ever seen a river cut a valley. Nor did anyone in those days have a clear notion about the water cycle, which every seventh-grader learns about today. The condensation-evaporation-condensation chain which, with the help of gravity, keeps water moving from sea to land to sea again was simple in principle but not easy to witness.

James Hutton, the Scottish farmer, will be remembered as the first man to recognize the tremendous powers of erosion and the fact that they are operating today as in the past. After Hutton, one of the big tasks of geologists was to study rivers carefully and find out how they really work.

River with a task—Royal Gorge, in southern Colorado, has formed where Colorado River cuts through granite. Deep, narrow gorge is typical where stream is swift and walls are highly resistant to erosion. Down-cutting is faster than erosion of walls.

by the waters of a third. The three-brooks-in-one feel their way along the valley bottom for a mile and then empty into a stream that already carries the waters of a dozen brooks. And this stream, a few miles farther on, pours into a full-fledged river, containing waters from a hundred brooks, drained from a thousand square miles of land.

So the joining of the waters—all moving downward—goes on. A day after our raindrops fall on the Pennsylvania hill, some are swept into the broad Allegheny. Two days later they are in the mighty Ohio River, sliding southwestward between the states of Ohio and Kentucky. In a few days more some have joined the mighty Mississippi.

For perhaps two weeks, the far-traveling raindrops follow the turns and loops of the Father of Waters, working ever southward. At last, perhaps a month after they fell from the sky, these raindrops — from thirty-one states, covering 1,244,000 square miles—pour into the Gulf of Mexico.

Rough going—*Rapids like these, and worse, in Grand Canyon of Colorado River were negotiated by Major Powell and party in 1869. Brown with rock debris, river here is cutting through sandstone.*

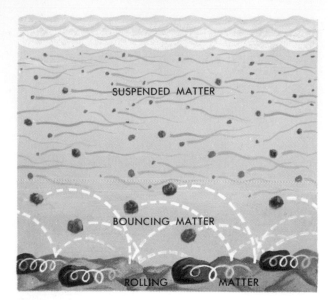

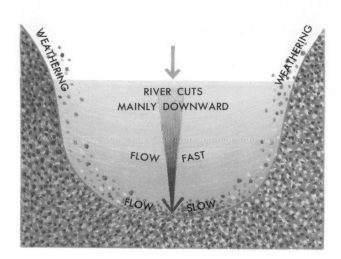

Cross Section—*Force of flow is able to carry lightest material, such as silt, in suspension, while heavier material such as sand and light gravel bounces along. Cobbles and boulders are rolled or remain stationary. Some may become undermined.*

Lengthwise Section—*Cutting is mainly downward. Friction with shores and bottom slows flow; flow is fastest near middle. River banks are steadily cut back by surface erosion—frost, surface water, activities of plants and animals.*

A RIVER'S CHANNEL

Suppose a river, moving at a speed of one mile per hour, can carry grains of sand and roll pebbles as big as marbles along its bottom. At two miles per hour it can carry small bits of gravel for short distances, and roll stones as large as golf balls. Make the speed four miles per hour and that river will be carrying much larger bits of gravel, and rolling cobbles as big as oranges.

As the speed of water increases, its ability to carry rock waste grows much faster than one might think. That is the secret of the power of rivers to carve their channels and help to shape entire landscapes.

Everyone knows that water has pushing and sucking power. But it cannot, by itself, cut. For cutting work it depends mainly on rock waste. As the human hand uses a file to grind away steel, rivers use sand, gravel, and pebbles to grind their channels.

While rock waste is doing the grinding, the water itself pushes, plucks, and sucks at the bottom of the channel and at the sides. It dissolves minerals out of the rock and mud. Gravity pulls down loose material from the edges of the channel, adding it to the river's bed load. And so the channel gradually deepens and widens.

A channel through hard rock, such as granite, may deepen only an inch or two in 100 years. A channel on soft rock, such as shale, may deepen a foot in a few months.

The river's freight of sand, gravel, and pebbles is not kept moving at all times. The load that the river can keep moving depends on the speed of the current. In dry seasons the current has little strength, and the heavier parts of the load are dropped in the channel, where they form bars and perhaps islands. In times of rain and melting snows, much of the load will be picked up again. If the river floods over its banks, some of the rock waste will be carried over the countryside and dropped there as so-called "alluvial" deposits.

If a river channel is narrow and rock-filled, pebbles and cobbles cannot be easily rolled. But whatever the resistance to the water's progress, it will get by. Sooner or later, by the trick of undermining, it will move even great boulders that block its way.

TURNING THE CORNERS

As river water moves around a bend, the water on the inside of the curve slows down and drops part of its load. Rock material piles up there. On the outside the water is going faster, like a boy on

the end of a snap-the-whip. The water strikes the outside bank hard, gouging sand and pebbles out of it, and then hurries on.

The river keeps exerting most of its force straight ahead. Therefore the outside bank of a curve is where the river hits hardest. That bank tends to get worn back faster than the others. By wearing back the outside bank on curves, most rivers tend to straighten out in time.

The outside bank may wear back until it meets a curve of the river farther downstream. The water may then move directly through the new channel—a short cut. The old channel often becomes an oxbow lake. Many such lakes are seen along the southern stretches of the Mississippi.

ROUGH WATER

Wherever the slope of the channel gets steeper, the water moves faster. Where the channel runs through soft rock, it usually widens, and the river tends to slow down. In hard rock the channel usually is narrower, and the flow faster.

Down a steep slope—for instance, 15 feet downward for every 100 feet forward—the water will rush along violently, perhaps tumbling boulders along with it, forming rapids.

In a rough channel, with water flowing fast around rocks, whirlpools form. Water glancing off a rock starts spinning as it is hit by other water rushing by. Any material caught up into the whirlpool will spin likewise. In time, spinning sand and pebbles may make potholes, some of which could become several yards in diameter.

Looping the loops—*Christian River, lazily crossing a plain in Alaska, keeps changing course in seeking way of least resistance. Many abandoned loops are visible. River's phase is that of "old age."*

Fans in Death Valley, California—*Where ravines in Panamint Mountains reach valley, typical fan-shaped deposits of rock debris are seen. Debris is carried down by water, dropped where slope eases.*

LOST RIVERS AND FANS

Some rivers follow a course on the surface of the earth for many miles, and then suddenly vanish underground. Miles away, perhaps, at a lower level, they appear again. Such rivers are common in regions where the bedrocks are of limestone, as in Kentucky.

Some streams, as they come down from mountains or hills, flow out into a desert. Here the water table is likely to be very far down. Then the river may flow out into the desert only a short distance before it disappears.

Mountain rivers are generally swift, and able to carry big loads of rock waste. But as they come down into the valleys, they lose speed abruptly and drop their freight. At the foot of a mountain ravine or gully, therefore, we generally see a "fan"

—a triangular deposit of rock waste. At the point of the fan are the largest rocks, which were dropped first, and at the outside edges are the smallest particles, which were dropped last.

WHY WATERFALLS?

Occasionally a river channel comes to a cliff. The water tumbles over, forming a waterfall, and then goes on its way. Waterfalls are generally favorite spots for the scenery, but unfortunately they are somewhat unusual. They can form only under certain conditions. And rivers, so it seems, work hard to eliminate their waterfalls.

Most waterfalls owe their existence to hard rock strata overlying soft. An example is Niagara Falls. As the Niagara River reaches the falls, it is flowing over a layer of hard limestone. Under that

Future of Niagara Falls—*Each dotted line shows contour of falls at a future stage. Falls can exist only as long as there is the layer of hard rock to overhang soft rock beneath.*

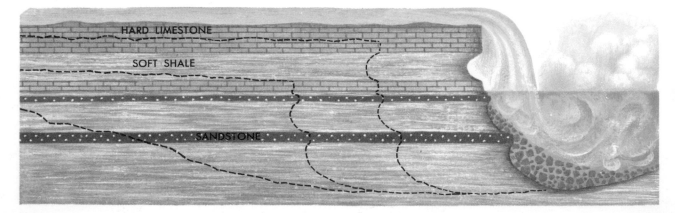

HARD LIMESTONE

SOFT SHALE

SANDSTONE

Yellowstone's Lower Falls—Drop of 308 feet occurs where river waters, flowing over hard stratum, abruptly met softer rock and cut into it more swiftly.

layer are softer rocks, including shale. As the water goes over the falls, some of it is dashed against the soft rocks, which erode more rapidly than the limestone. The limestone layer becomes undermined, and overhangs develop. Now and then a block of overhanging limestone falls. Thus the process goes on, and as more of the soft rock is cut away and more of the overhanging rock breaks off, the falls retreats upstream.

Niagara Falls is retreating toward Lake Erie at the rate of four to five feet per year, but the falls will never reach Lake Erie. When the falls is about two miles upstream from where it is now, the river will have cut completely through the hard limestone and will be cutting into the shale. Overhangs will no longer develop. The cliff will turn into a slope, and instead of falls there will be rapids.

WANDERING WATERS

Some rivers idle down broad valleys of gentle slope. Their banks are low, their channels wide. The Mississippi below Cairo, Illinois, is a river of this type. So is the Mohawk River in New York.

Accidental scenery—Splendid Niagara Falls, like all other waterfalls, is a geological accident and will be short-lived. These are the American Falls, seen from a tour boat on the river.

In a time of melting snows or heavy rains, such rivers may receive more waters than their channels can contain. Water floods over the low banks, drowning farmers' fields, washing out sections of highways, and sweeping away houses. Millions of dollars' worth of destruction may result.

During the rampage, the river may spread enormous amounts of sand and silt, or "alluvium," over lowlands nearby. As fresh, fertile soil it may be welcomed by farmers. Some material dropped by flood waters may pile up near the river in long ridges, called natural levees. These will limit the spread of the water, up to a certain point, in times of future flooding.

A flooding river may make new channels for itself. Some rivers, like the Mississippi in Louisiana, have formed a broad network of such channels over the lowlands. Channels may loop miles beyond the river. In a rainy season they are full of running water, but in other periods they may dry up, leaving only still, lonely pools here and there.

HOW DELTAS FORM

As river water arrives at a lake or sea, it loses speed and starts dropping its load. The heavier material falls first, and the lightest last. The tiniest particles of clay and of plant and animal waste— so light that they have hardly any weight at all— do not fall until the water comes practically to a standstill. This may be in a quiet cove or bay, or may be miles out on the sea bottom.

End of the journey—*Here, on sprawling delta, Mississippi drops debris from a million square miles.*

The piled-up waste material at the mouth of a river takes a form usually like that of the Greek letter Δ, delta. So that is what the deposit is called.

For thousands or millions of years, the delta keeps growing outward. Meanwhile the water keeps a channel open all the way to the tip. In flood periods, water overflowing the river banks makes new sideward channels.

Mixed with rock waste in a delta there are usually large quantities of plant and animal waste. These make the delta fertile. Wherever one finds a delta, rich farms also are often seen.

THE RIVER THAT MADE A STATE

Each year, the Mississippi dumps onto its delta around 140 million tons of dissolved minerals, 400 million tons of sand and silt, and 60 million tons of rock material that has been rolled along the bottom. When we realize that great river systems such as the Mississippi's last for millions of

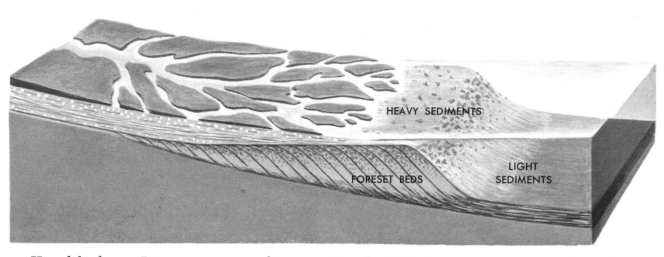

How delta forms—*River waters carry sediments out to end of delta, dropping coarse material first, then finer sediments farther out. In dry periods heavier sediments are dropped before reaching end of delta.*

years, we begin to appreciate what "erosion of the continents" really means. Every continent except Antarctica has such river systems.

That part of the Mississippi delta which is south of Baton Rouge, Louisiana, is the work of only a few thousand years. Yet it may be five to six miles deep. This depth is not apparent, because the weight of the deposits has caused the bottom of the Gulf of Mexico here to sink.

A few thousand years is only a moment in the life of the Mississippi. This great artery is millions of years old. Again and again it has changed course in its broad valley. During the recent ice ages, it carried glacial meltwaters from the Great Lakes to the Gulf. Once it flowed faster and cut more rapidly than today—its present bed is being lowered by erosion about a foot every 5,500 years. The present delta was begun only after the river had filled in an old bay covering the area that is now Louisiana. Residents can truthfully say that they owe their state to the river.

EGYPT'S BREADBASKET

The most famous delta in the world is that of the Nile. Here the river waters, after a 4,000-mile journey from Uganda, to the south, empty into the Mediterranean. Upon the delta, as well as along its banks in Lower Egypt, the Nile for many thousands of years has been dropping loads of minerals and plant refuse. It was this excellent river-laid soil, with the mild climate, that made possible the great civilization of ancient Egypt.

In the fifth century B.C., the famous Greek historian and traveler Herodotus visited Egypt. Like many other Greeks of old, Herodotus had an open, inquiring mind, and he found much to fascinate him in this land which had already been civilized for twenty centuries. He explored the delta of the Nile, studied the signs of the annual

87

flooding, went boating on the river, and talked about the delta with the Egyptian priests, who were the learned men of that country. In his *Histories,* Herodotus calculates that the delta took ten to twenty thousand years to form. This was a remarkably accurate guess in an era of history when most scholars would have guessed the age of the world as a few thousand years at most.

During the past thousand years, Egypt's coastal region has sunk, and part of the old delta is now covered by the sea. There is still, however, a vast expanse of delta being farmed. This fertile land, laced with irrigation canals, reaches from the Mediterranean shore as far south as Cairo. On the delta and along the river banks above, most of Egypt's twenty million people are concentrated.

RIVER VALLEYS

It was once supposed that rivers flow in valleys made for them by the rumpling of Earth's crust. Some rivers do flow in ready-made valleys, but most make their own.

The river works mainly to *deepen* its channel. Most of the widening is done by other forces, such as rain, air, frost, gravity, and the activities of plants and animals. In time, what began as just a river channel becomes a wide valley.

The form that the valley takes depends mostly upon the speed of the river. A swift river tends to make for a steep-sided valley. That is because the rate of down-cutting of the river is rapid compared to the erosion on the sides of the valley.

While the valley is being developed, the sinking of part of it may create waterfalls or a lake. Rising of part of the valley may stop the flow of the river and send it off in another direction. If the climate becomes wetter, the river may become more powerful. If times grow dryer, the water table may fall and the river may wane to a trickle.

Some river valleys have the odd fate of becoming "drowned." This happens where a seacoast sinks or the sea level rises. Ocean water creeps up into the valleys, forming what are called estuaries.

FIORDS

A special type of drowned river valley is the fiord. Many fiords are seen in far northern lands such as Norway, Finland, and Greenland.

Mature dignity—*White River in the Ozarks, southwestern Missouri, is a "mature" stream. Swelled by rains, it has flooded over its banks and, as shown by its color, is loaded with rock waste.*

Ready-made river valley—*Oneonta Gorge, in northwestern Oregon, started as joint in bedrock strata. Swift stream is now cutting it deeper.*

During the ice ages of the past million years, when so much of Earth's water was locked up in the great ice sheets, the level of the ocean was 200 to 300 feet lower than it is now. The river valleys on seacoasts of northern countries were full of ice, grinding its way seaward. As the last glacial period ended, the melting of tremendous masses of ice all over northern lands raised the level of the sea, and the sea invaded the coastal valleys.

The fiords, with the U-shape typical of glaciated valleys, still show glacial gouges and scratches on their steep walls. On their bottoms are heaps of sand and gravel dropped by the melting ice.

RIVERS YOUNG AND OLD

In speaking of rivers and their valleys, geologists often use the expressions "youth," "maturity," and "old age." They refer not to ages in years, but to phases of development.

A young river is one of steep grade, in a steep-sided valley. Usually it is rapid, twisting, and has few streams running into it. It may have many stretches of falls and rapids. The Colorado where it runs through the Grand Canyon is a good example of a young river.

After long erosion, the river is at the mature stage. It has lost grade and is now more leisurely; its valley is wider. Old age is the phase when the stream winds lazily through land that has been worn down almost to a flat plain. Everyone has seen examples of rivers in all these stages of development.

A river may be at different stages of development at different points along its course. Where it flows idly through a wide valley, it is "old." Then, abruptly, it may enter a region with a steeper slope, move faster in a narrow but deep channel, and thus become "young."

An old valley, with a lazy stream, may be lifted and tilted by a general rise in the land of the region. As the rising occurs—and this may take hundreds or thousands of years—the river gains

Drowned river valley—*Fiords, like this one in Norway seacoast, are river valleys that were invaded by rising sea waters as ice ages ended.*

speed. That gives it new power, and it cuts faster. Thus, like the San Juan and Colorado Rivers in some parts of their courses, it may cut a deep, narrow valley into a broad, level landscape. Such a river is "rejuvenated," or made young again.

MOUNTAINS CUT BY RIVERS

Some rivers, oddly enough, seem to have cut a channel right through a mountain range instead of going around it. The Shoshone River, where it

where the ancient Appalachians soared. The folded strata of the mountains were long ago eroded down to mere "stumps," and these were covered by sedimentary rocks laid down during an invasion by the sea. The Susquehanna cuts straight across and through the buried mountain folds. However, the smaller streams running into this river from both sides make channels that follow the folds, digging deep where the rock is weak and less deep where the folds are more resistant. In time, as erosion cuts down the whole region, the roots of the old mountain range become exposed, and we have not only the main river cutting through the range, but the tributaries splitting it with valleys. Such "dissection" is seen in many old mountain ranges.

RIVER PIRATES

Rivers sometimes engage in "piracy." This happens when the valley being cut by one river meets the valley of another river. A contest begins between the rivers for the available water supply. The river that wins—that is, the "pirate"—is the one which has a big enough channel and steep enough slope to make it more efficient as a water carrier and channel cutter. The other valley is left with only a trickle for a river—or no river at all.

Sometimes a river builds natural levees along its banks, and a neighboring stream may be unable to penetrate these barriers. A familiar example of one stream that is fended off by another

slices through the Absaroka Range in Wyoming, is an example.

Once this river flowed across a plain. Gradually, underground forces caused the plain to bulge up in the middle; but as the bulge grew, the river kept cutting into it and thus maintained a channel. Finally, the bulge was a full-fledged mountain range—with a river neatly cutting it in two. The valley through the range is called a water gap.

The Susquehanna River system is in a region

Youth: *Rise of land gives river steep grade. Flow is rapid. River lacks tributaries; valley is narrow and irregular; and waterfalls occur.*

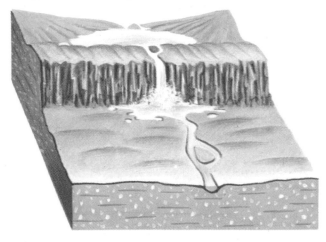

Early maturity: *Erosion has reduced elevation. Flow is now slower, valley wider. Tributaries have developed. Valley sediments (brown) are building up.*

Rejuvenated river—Thousands of years ago, San Juan River was lazy meander on plain. Then land rose, river's grade steepened, and rapid downward cutting began. "Gooseneck" is near Medicine Hat, southern Utah.

one is the Yazoo in the state of Mississippi. Only after running parallel to the Mississippi River for a long stretch does the Yazoo finally succeed in joining it—at Vicksburg.

In regions such as the Appalachians, where river systems have been at work for many millions of years, without serious disturbance by movements of Earth's crust, geologists find what they call "maturely dissected" landscapes. Here careful detective work can trace out histories of piracy and other maneuvers of running water over stretches of a hundred million years.

Later maturity: *Erosion has further reduced grade. Flow is still slower, valley wider. Original landscape is much softened. River has developed broad flood plain, through which it is wandering.*

Old age: *Landscape has been eroded almost to a plain. Original features are gone. Grade of river is slight; flow is slow. River is meandering even more widely and developing oxbows.*

Rivers of Ice

The higher slopes of most big mountain ranges of the world—the Alps, the Canadian Rockies, the Himalayas—are white all year. In deep mountain hollows, the snows do not melt or blow away; they are hundreds of feet deep. On the surface the snow is soft, but underneath it is harder-packed, because of the great weight above. Toward the bottom, pressure has turned the oldest snows—the snows of centuries past—into hard pellets and solid masses of ice.

That ice is rock—real rock which just happens to melt at a lower temperature than other kinds of rocks. It is hard and stiff and strong; but even as rock it cannot withstand the awful weight of hundreds of feet of packed snow and ice above. It bulges at the bottom, like a mud pie. It bulges over the edges of the hollows and flows down the mountainsides. It forms glaciers.

Scientists have argued for a hundred years about how a glacier moves. Most agree that the glacier's own weight causes the ice pellets to roll, the ice crystals to bend and slip against each other, and the ice masses to slide. Also, as pressure causes some of the ice to melt, the water moves to some other place in the glacier where there is less pressure, and freezes there. Thus a glacier moves.

A glacier is a destroyer whose work begins in the mountain hollow where it is born. Edges of the glacier keep freezing to the rocky walls of the hollow and then breaking loose again, yanking out chunks of rock as they do so. Years of this plucking action turn the hollow into a large, rounded half-bowl called a cirque.

Leaving the cirque, the ice follows a ravine or valley down the mountain. On the way, it cuts a channel as a river does. But even with its speed of

Panorama of ice—*Columbia Glacier, one of Alaska's finest, gathers ice from scores of tributary glaciers inland. Arriving at Pacific shore, its front is 5 miles wide, 200 feet high.*

only a few inches or feet per day, its strength dwarfs that of any river. Shoulders of bedrock in the channel are rammed, yanked, and broken as the ice goes by. Rocks falling on the glacier's broad back gradually press their way down through the ice. Rocks broken loose from the bottom of the channel are dragged along as scrapers to deepen the channel further.

CREVASSES, ICEFALLS, AND THE GLACIAL RIVER

When the ice comes to a hump in its course, it moves over stiffly, and the bending strain breaks the glacier's back into rows of cracks called crevasses. Where the valley widens, the glacier's weight causes it to spread outward to fill the extra space, and more crevasses open up.

Here and there, the ice moves over a low spot, or dip, in its channel. There is an enormous squeezing strain in the top of the glacier and a stretching strain in the bottom. That may cause further breakage of the ice.

The iceflow may come to a precipice hundreds or thousands of feet high. Pieces of ice break off and drop in what is called an icefall. Striking and shattering, far below, they form there another iceflow. Downward the flow continues, seeking lower and lower levels.

Parts of the glacier keep rubbing and knocking against each other and against the sides and bottom of the channel. The pressure and friction make enough heat to cause some of the ice to melt, even if the temperature is below freezing. Meltwaters run down through the crevasses and join other water to form a river beneath the glacier. This river, plunging down and down through its deep blue ice tunnel, tumbles a load of rock waste along with it, and digs the valley deeper.

93

Alpine *"white rivers"—Ice from packed snows of centuries creeps down Mt. Blanc, France.*

GLACIER'S END

The deadly enemy of all glaciers is heat—heat from the Sun. Direct sunlight, or air warmed by it, causes some melting of the ice. Also, some ice evaporates directly into the air without first melting. A glacier can continue to exist only if it keeps getting enough new snow during the year to make up for what it loses by melting and evaporation.

In temperate lands, enough snow falls on high mountains in winter to replace what is lost in summer. In the Alps there are no fewer than 1,200 glaciers "in business." In North America's Rockies there are large glaciers as far south as Montana, and smaller ones down as far as the Grand Tetons of Wyoming and the Sierra Nevada of California.

During winter in these regions, snow piles up on the glaciers. Melting and evaporation are slight. Gradually, the tips of the glaciers creep down the mountain ravines. But when spring comes, this movement is reversed. The rates of melting and evaporation increase, and the bottom tips of the glaciers melt off faster than the down-ward flow. The tips keep retreating—melting back—until autumn, with its new snowfalls and lower temperatures.

In warm seasons, the bottom edge of a glacier is soft and crumbling. From beneath it rushes a torrent of meltwaters. Down, down rushes this glacial river, carrying gravel and sand with it—a load which is scattered finally on the valley floor.

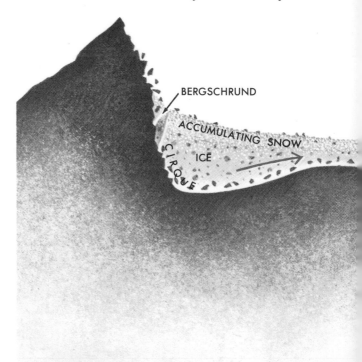

94

Ice fantasy—Meltwaters from Paradise Glacier, on western slope of Mt. Rainier, Washington, carved ice chamber and arch. Note glacial river and accumulated rock debris in riverbed.

PIEDMONT GLACIERS AND
ICE SHEETS

On its way down a mountain valley, one glacier may join another, just as rivers do. At the point of junction there is a great pushing and cracking and grinding, but somehow they combine, and a larger iceflow continues downward. At the base of some mountain ranges, numbers of glaciers run together to form one large sheet called a piedmont (French for "foot of the mountain") glacier.

Anatomy of glacier—*Diagram shows how ice forms in cirque, grinds downward through its valley, and dies away at warmer levels below. At far right icebergs are being formed where glacier reaches sea.*

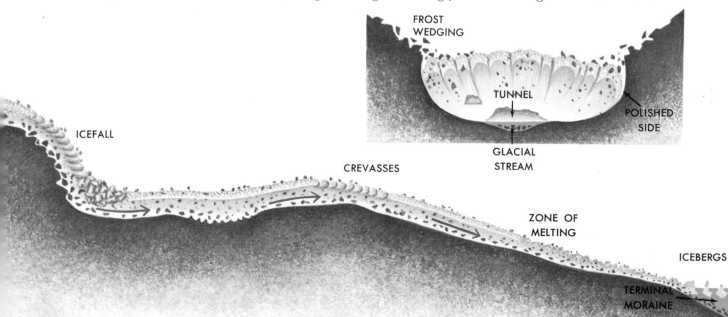

"Calving"—As glacier meets waters of Portage Lake, Alaska, chunks break off front to become icebergs.

Icefall—Climbers in Alps pause to look where glacier goes over precipice to form Stockje Icefall.

In very cold lands, such as Greenland and Antarctica, the amount of snow that falls during the year is greater than the amount that melts. The ice moving down the mountain valleys joins other flows and forms a broad sheet that covers the land completely, or nearly so. This sheet, pressed down by new snows and pushed by ice flowing from the mountains, spreads steadily outward. The edges of the sheet reach the ocean at some points. There, as the ice moves out into the water, it is buoyed up by the water, and the bending strain causes it to break off in chunks.

These ice chunks are carried out to sea by winds and currents, and are seen by shipboard travelers as icebergs. Icebergs are the snows of hundreds or thousands of years ago, brought at last by gravity down to the sea.

THE AGES OF ICE

For uncounted centuries, men in northern lands have been neighbors to glaciers. Prehistoric peoples in Europe and Asia lived along the great ice fronts, where reindeer, mammoth, and smaller game were abundant. In our day in Europe, North America, and Asia, communities thrive where the mountains are white the year around, and melting ice waters the valleys and feeds the glistening lakes. It is natural to suppose that the world's glaciers have always been about what they are today.

Science has known otherwise, however, since 1837. In that year a young Swiss zoologist, an expert on fishes, an Alpine hiker with a sharp eye, delivered a historic lecture before the Helvetic Society, a scientific group, in Switzerland. With a very certain air he announced that the glaciers of today are the remains of much greater ones of the past. Long ago, said Louis Agassiz to his unbelieving audience, great ice sheets spread down from the pole and blanketed the northern hemisphere as far south as central Europe and Asia.

Where had young Agassiz picked up such a notion? All this sounded like too much imagination and too little experience in science!

Under an ice cliff—Flowers bloom at edge of ice sheet in Etah area, Greenland. As far south as New York, London, and Berlin, prehistoric man lived along similar ice cliffs during recent glacial ages.

Horn mountain—Switzerland's famed Matterhorn is typical horn mountain, shaped by converging glaciers that planed off sides. Ice was once at least as high as present summit. Zermatt is in foreground.

The year before, in the Alps, two friends had pointed out to him the tell-tale signs of glaciers—moraines and scratched boulders — in valleys where glaciers had not reached during the whole known span of history. First with interest, then with growing excitement, Agassiz had explored glaciers, seen how they formed and advanced and melted, and then examined the iceless slopes and valleys below. His doubts had faded. Yes, ice did once fill these quiet valleys of central Europe. It must have covered all the northern lands!

The response of scientists to Agassiz's declaration was: "Nonsense!"

But as with Guettard and Demarest, Hutton and Lyell, the last word was with those who could point to overwhelming evidence. That evidence was scattered all over central and northern Europe: heaped moraines of sand and gravel, ice-battered rocks scattered through U-shaped valleys, ice-gouged mountain ravines, amphitheater-like mountain hollows where ancient snows had piled up and glaciers had begun their downward journeys.

The study of glaciers, neglected before Agassiz, now became popular, and Agassiz soon had a large following. The reality of Earth's ancient cold ages was accepted.

Agassiz later went to America. During his great twenty-seven-year career at Harvard University, he found time to explore areas of North America where, as in Europe, giant hands of ice had worked long ago.

THREE MILES THICK

More than a century has passed since Agassiz shocked the Helvetic Society. Since then the story of past ice ages—there have been many, not just one—has been carefully pieced together.

The last glacial period occurred during the past million years. Four different times, apparently, great domes of ice formed on the northern parts of North America, Europe, and Asia; they spread outward and then melted back again. In North America, one big mass formed on eastern

Living glacier—Typical cirque is seen in this view of Columbia Icefield, Jasper National Park, Canada.

PACIFIC OCEAN

ATLANTIC OCEAN

The great ice sheets—*Map shows regions covered by ice during glacial periods of past million years.*

ice was a mile, and the flow down the Mississippi Valley was two to three miles deep. In the West, there were mountain glaciers as far south as New Mexico. From Alaska to Lower California, and from Greenland to Cuba, the oceans were crowded with icebergs.

As the ice inched southward over Canada, it sliced the tops off hills and gouged sixty to seventy-five feet of soil and bedrock out of the Canadian plains. It flattened forests, obliterated rivers, and forced wildlife to retreat southward. Its meltwaters, working through heaps of boulders, plant remains, and ground-up rock at the glacier's edges, opened channels that are now followed by the Ohio and other rivers that feed the Mississippi in the north central states.

Beneath the blue ice cliffs and in the shadows of the evergreen forests, life went on as it does in arctic lands today. Where Denver and Chicago and Philadelphia now stand, the musk-ox grazed

Canada, another west of Hudson Bay, and another along the Rockies. When the climate was coldest, these masses joined to form one enormous sheet covering all of Canada and reaching south in long tongues as far as where St. Louis, Missouri, stands today. The average thickness of the

Ice exit—*Ice accumulating in White Mountains, New Hampshire, during glacial periods ground its way out onto nearby lowlands, carving broad valleys on way. U-shaped path here is Crawford Notch.*

Once an ice channel—*In glacial ages Yosemite Valley was full of ice. Ice-flow planed off vertical wall of El Capitan (left) and cut away half of mass of granite now called Half Dome (background, center).*

among alpine meadows and drank from icy streams. Among its neighbors were mammoths and mastodons, the great royal bison, and wild horses. Farther south, in retreat, were animals now being driven either into extinction or to a life in warmer South America: ancestors of the camels and tapirs, the ground sloth, the sabertooth cat and the great wolf.

In northern Europe and Siberia, there was the same drama of advancing ice and retreating living things. Along the ice fronts lived mastodon and mammoth, reindeer and woolly rhinoceros, and the giant cave bear. Farther to the south, retreating from the ice, were tapirs, elephants, rhinoceroses, and hosts of other animals that had thrived in northern Europe before the ice came. These creatures of milder climates were pushed farther and farther south by the advancing glaciers. The descendants of many of them are found in southern Asia and Africa today.

THE HAIRLESS HUNTER

One of the creatures that faced the marching ice in northern Europe and Asia was a newcomer of extreme cleverness. No one knows just where he came from, or exactly when, but there he was, holding his own. Along the ice fronts, groups of these almost hairless, brown-skinned creatures hunted the reindeer and the mammoth with spears. Learning in ways that are beyond ordinary animals, the newcomers thrived through the glacial ages and became masters of their world.

As the ice sheets retreated for the last time, 8,000 to 10,000 years ago, primitive men were scattered all over the Old World. They were using fire, painting pictures in caves, and burying their dead.

Perhaps just before the last glacial advance—say, 35,000 years ago—ancient men in northeast Asia wandered onto a neck of land leading to the region we call Alaska. Over they went, and they

Scored by passing ice—*Bedrock in Flathead National Forest, Montana, shows deep glacial grooves. Scratched and grooved rocks, evidence of glaciers, are found as far south as New Jersey, southern Ohio, and New Mexico.*

plodded southward, finding a path between the partly melted ice domes. Today their spearpoints and the remains of their campfires are found in caves and old streambeds of the Southwest.

THE LAST RETREAT

As the ice melted northward, new forests grew up and animals moved in to take over the land once more. But the marks of the ice were there, and would be for thousands of years to come.

In the present areas of Minnesota, northern Michigan, Maine, and central Canada, glacial lakes filled countless hollows gouged out by the ice. Soil and rock scraped off Canada and carried south by the ice lay strewn over the central United States—there to become rich land for farmers of the future.

On the East Coast, an enormous heap of sand and gravel, stretching 100 miles out into the sea, was left where an ice front dropped it—Long Island. Farther north, a dwindling ice front left enough sands and clays to make Cape Cod. From the Atlantic to the Rockies, hills of sand and gravel marked the spots where ice cliffs once towered, then crumbled away.

The ice is still melting back. Central Canada, scraped bare in places, is now a sunny land, not a bleak ice field. In western Canada, ice persists throughout the year only in the mountains. In the east, only the Greenland ice sheet remains, rising 8,000 feet above the island, its edges feeding icebergs to the sea.

Makings for stone walls—*Some areas of northern North America and Europe are littered with rock debris dropped by melting ice of glaciers.*

Glacier's birthplace—*Cirque in Giant Mountain in Adirondacks, New York, is one of many in region.*

Earth's climates continue to grow warmer. Most of the world's glaciers are retreating. The Greenland glacier is shrinking, and its bergs do not last as long as they did a generation ago in their southward Atlantic voyage. In the Alps and in the mountains of Norway, the mountain glaciers each summer melt back just a little farther than they did the summer before. The melting ice of the world is raising the level of the sea two inches per year. The fourth glacial age is ending.

WILL THE ICE COME BACK?

The ice could come back. A drop of 10 degrees in average northern hemisphere temperatures might allow the ice, in a few hundred years, to pile up and cover Paris, London, and New York—even areas farther south—once more. The ice has returned before, and can again.

Suppose, however, that climates get warmer until all the mountain glaciers and the polar ice have melted away. That would mean a crisis almost as serious as a new ice age. For something like 3¼ million cubic miles of the earth's water is still locked up in this ice. The Antarctic ice cap

alone is 9,000 feet thick over the pole and covers millions of square miles. If all the ice in the world melts, the oceans will rise about 250 feet and drown out the world's great seaport cities!

Strange to say, a *warming up* of the arctic regions might cause a new glacial age. If the ice that now chokes the Arctic Ocean melted, a great deal of ocean water would be exposed to evaporation. The extra moisture in the air could increase the amount of snowfall in the north and cause the existing ice caps to grow and spread. Some geologists think this is what actually happened during the most recent glacial ages.

Studying a glacier—*From Antarctica to north polar regions, glaciers are under study by enterprising scientists. Here, a party of glaciologists is camped on Juneau Icefield, Alaska.*

Once under water—*Sandstone in South Dakota's Badlands dates from about 40 million years ago, when shallow waters covered region. It is rich in fossils.*

New Rocks from Old

THE WORK of running water, gravity, frost, wind, and air may seem completely destructive, yet it is creative too. These very forces that destroy the old rocks keep piling up the debris to make new ones: the sedimentary rocks. The creation, destruction, and re-creation of rocks is a sort of unending merry-go-round process in the story of Earth.

Erosion is an obvious process. Even prehistoric man may have contemplated the gully in the hillside, the muddy waters of a river in flood, the heaps of stone fallen to the foot of a cliff. But far less obvious is the process by which erosion debris —or, for that matter, the remains of animals and plants—can be made into solid rock. One man in his lifetime can witness rock-making only in a few special cases, such as the formation of stalactites in a cave or the hardening of a lava flow. No wonder the making of sedimentary rocks became part of human knowledge only recently.

Several of the ancient Greeks, such as Anaximander, who lived in the seventh century B.C., noticed fossils in limestone quarries and ventured to say that these were the remains of real animals and plants, buried originally in soft sediments which later turned to stone. In the sixteenth century, Leonardo da Vinci, who was so quick to trace cause and effect, decided for himself not only that fossils had once lived, but that such ancient life forms had been buried on sea bottoms by mud carried down into the sea by rivers, and that the rocks formed from this mud had later become—by some unknown process—land surfaces in Europe. But at the opening of the 1800's, most people still thought of Earth as having been specially created, in one grand act, by a divine hand. The notion that the rocks had taken form by natural processes seemed very odd. Where it

seemed absolutely obvious that some rocks *had* formed in water, people could fall back upon the Bible's story of Noah's flood.

The 1800's were past the halfway mark before the origins of the main groups of rocks— igneous, sedimentary, and metamorphic—were well distinguished from one another. Scientific classifications became possible only with steady advances in chemical analysis and long, careful observation by geologists in the field.

Even today, the argument goes on among geologists as to whether most of the granites were once molten or are, on the contrary, sedimentary rocks that have been changed by heat, pressure, and infiltration by other substances.

ROCKS FROM WRECKS

The sedimentary rocks are more common on our planet's surface than any other type of bedrocks. Never having been molten, they usually

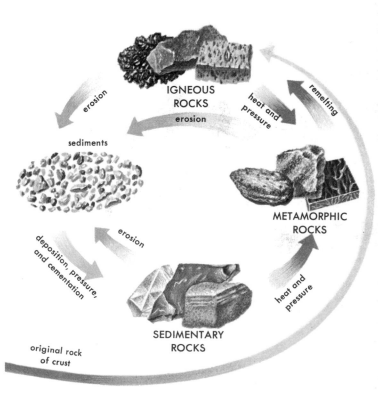

Rock cycle—Most sedimentary rocks form from waste of other rocks. Some consist of remains of plants and animals. Diagram indicates relationships of sedimentary rocks to other types.

Where sedimentary rocks may form—*Rock debris from highlands piles up in valleys to form conglomerates, sandstones, and shales. Clays dropped on lake and river bottoms harden into shale. On lake bottoms and seashores, rivers drop sediments to form more sandstones and shales. On sea bottom, limy ooze packs to form limestone.*

CONGLOMERATE

LIMESTONE

SHALE

SANDSTONE

SHALE

LIMESTONE

look quite different from igneous rocks. They are mostly lighter in weight and lighter in color. When seen in the face of a cliff, they ordinarily have a neat, layered appearance like that of a wall built of long blocks or sheets. The lines between the layers may look like marks made by changing levels of water. The color and texture of the rock may change gradually or abruptly from layer to layer. The layers may be slanted.

These rocks are made from the wastes of the world—bits of eroded rock, remains of plants and animals, particles of minerals left by water. Most

were formed in water, but some are of materials deposited by wind.

Many of these rocks are made of sand grains, and some are full of pebbles. There are the gray, bluish, and white limestones, in the form of bulky blocks, masses of shells, or solid chalky deposits. Most common are the shales and siltstones—rock in the form of thin sheets that crumble into tiny grains of clay.

The sedimentary rocks lie over the granite continents like giant patchwork quilts, with holes here and there, and they form some parts, too, of the ocean floor. They are found in lowlands and in the loftiest mountain peaks. Sedimentary rocks are, in fact, the rocks out of which most mountain ranges have been made.

THE ROCK FACTORY

Sediments, the debris of erosion on Earth, tend to get washed or blown into valleys and sea bottoms. Some are soon carried away again, but elsewhere they pile up, age after age. As they reach thicknesses of hundreds or even thousands of feet, the lower layers get pressed and packed harder and harder. Water may trickle through them, carrying minerals that cement the particles together. Gradually the sediments become rock.

The process is usually very slow. The formation of two feet of shale in a hundred years would be regarded by geologists as rapid. It would not

MEDIUM-GRAINED SANDSTONE

RED SANDSTONE (cemented by iron oxide)

ARKOSE (showing feldspar grains)

Ripple Marks in Sandstone

"CRAB ORCHARD" SANDSTONE

be unusual for two feet of limestone to take six thousand years to form—more time than is spanned by all of written human history, more time than has elapsed since the Pyramids of Egypt were built.

STONE FROM GRAVEL, SAND, AND CLAY

Of all the sedimentary rocks, conglomerate is the coarsest. It is made mostly of gravel and pebbles, stuck together by some mineral, such as silica, acting as a cement. Some conglomerates are crumbly. Many contain pebbles of white quartz, which is a common mineral in granite, also. The usual places for conglomerates to form are in river beds at the foot of highlands and along beaches.

Sedimentary rocks that form from sand grains are the sandstones—some 20 per cent of all sedimentary rocks. Blocks of this kind of stone were much used, years ago, for the familiar "brownstone" houses in many cities. Most of the sand grains are just large enough to see with the unaided eye. White, pink, brown, and red are all colors characteristic of sandstones.

Sandstones are made mostly of quartz particles —usually rock waste from igneous rocks or other sandstones. The waste may have piled up in deserts, on river bottoms, or off seashores.

Water-made sandstone with large grains is likely to form where rapidly moving water slows down. This might occur, for example, where a river comes down into a valley, lake, or sea. Smaller-grained sands are likely to be deposited farther out.

A few sandstones began as sands piled up on the land—for example, the so-called frozen dunes in parts of the western United States. These dunes were buried by wind-blown material, turned to rock, and finally uncovered by erosion. Some show ripple marks made by winds millions of years ago. Many show crossbedding.

Shales, also called mudstones, are by far the most common sedimentary rocks, making up over 50 per cent of all. They have very fine grains,

"Frozen" dunes—*Winds blowing across southern Utah millions of years ago blew sand first one way, then another. Crossbedded formations are result.*

Wreck of mountains—*Chunks of limestone eroded from ancient Appalachians appear in conglomerate outcrop near Suffern, N. Y. Large cobble is foot long.*

105

Relic of old delta—*Shale in Catskill Mountains region, New York, was once clay on great delta.*

Once a sea bottom—*Limestone outcrops are seen near southern shore of Georgian Bay, Canada.*

which are of clay rather than quartz minerals, and often contain much plant material. The clay grains, smaller than those in sandstone, are deposited where moving water comes to a standstill. Lake beds, deltas, bays, and shallow seas are likely places.

THE STORY OF LIMESTONE

The fourth main kind of sedimentary rock is limestone. Some limestones have formed in fresh waters, but most were laid in warm, clear seas, far from the muddy mouths of rivers.

Limestone consists mostly of tiny particles of calcite (calcium carbonate), and is usually white, gray, or bluish. The harder formations are quar-

Common Types of Shale

OIL SHALE

CALCAREOUS SHALE
(Limy)

SANDY SHALE

ried for building stone. Portland cement is made from certain kinds of limestone mixed with shale.

Some limestones form from calcite particles that are precipitated—that is, dropped out of solution. Precipitation may be due to warming of the water, evaporation, or chemical action.

Other limestones are made up partly or even entirely of the skeletons, shells, or other limy remains of billions upon billions of ancient sea plants and animals. The limy material was originally in rocks of the land, then was dissolved out by water, next was carried to the sea, and was in turn used by plants and animals there to build their bodies. Finally, when they died, it was given back again to the sea.

Some limestone formations are in the form of reefs built up long ago by corals. Similar reefs are being built up today in warmer seas of the world, especially the South Pacific.

Chalk deposits, such as those exposed in Kansas and in the famous white cliffs of Dover, England, are limestones made up mostly of the remains of one-celled animals too small to see without a microscope.

Since they are made of odds and ends, sedimentary rocks are rarely "pure." Different combinations of sediments may join to form a shaly limestone or a limy shale, for example, or a sandy shale or a shaly sandstone.

106

Chalk rocks, Wind Canyon, South Dakota—*Limestone that makes blackboard chalk consists mostly of remains of tiny sea organisms called foraminifers. Dover Cliffs, England, are of similar origin.*

LAYER UPON LAYER

Where we see different kinds of sedimentary strata in a single series—for example, in a cliff—each layer represents a different set of environmental conditions under which the sediments were laid down. Thus shale at the bottom, then limestone, then shale again, and finally sandstone might represent a delta which became a sea bottom, then became a delta again, and finally became dry land. A change of 200 feet in sea level could account for such transformations. Any rock series, then, may represent a record of Earth history for a time at that place.

THE BATTLE OF THE ROCKS

Many a sea bottom loaded with shale and limestone has risen above sea level to become dry land and, eventually, a mountain range. Such movements usually involve bending, stretching, squeez-

Pages of a region's history—*Changes in strata, here seen in roadside cliff, eastern Utah, result from changes in environment as sediments were laid.*

Mountains from sediments—*Rocky Mountains, like many others, formed from sediments that became rock and were folded. Layering is apparent in mountains of Jasper National Park, Canada*

ing, folding, or cracking of the strata. From time to time, rising magma may force its way through or between the strata to form dikes and sills.

Pressure and heat can change rock in both appearance and chemical nature. For example, shale may be turned into slate, and slate into the shiny, flaky rock called mica schist. Rocks thus changed are said to be "metamorphosed."

Sedimentary rocks, like the others, suffer erosion, also. Usually softer than igneous rocks, they tend to wear away faster. In time, they are destroyed and scattered as rock waste—from which new rocks may form.

There is no telling how many times each little grain in a piece of sedimentary rock has gone through nature's ancient rock mixer.

PATCHWORKS AND SANDWICHES

More of Earth's crust is covered by sedimentary rocks than by igneous rocks. Probably every region on the continents has at some time been blanketed by sedimentary strata. Even so, there are places where no sedimentary rocks appear. They have been worn away, drowned by lava flows, covered with soil, or perhaps transformed by metamorphism.

Over all the continents the sedimentary strata lie in big patchworks. The formations that show on top differ from place to place, and were formed at different times. Beneath the surface stratum there are usually others, like slices of a many-decked sandwich. All have been warped, twisted, and folded to some extent. Together, they represent a sort of jigsaw puzzle for geologists.

In most parts of western North America the sedimentary strata are miles deep. Here and there they have been covered by sand, soil, and—especially in the Northwest—by deep lava flows. The Rocky Mountains reveal limestones, shales, and sandstones that formed on sea bottoms. At lower levels, from Montana to Arizona, we see shales and sandstones formed by rivers, lakes, and wind.

108

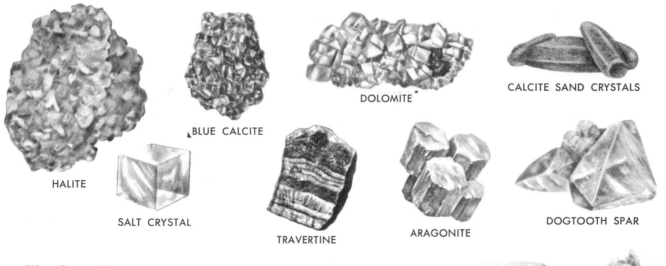

HALITE

BLUE CALCITE

DOLOMITE

CALCITE SAND CRYSTALS

SALT CRYSTAL

TRAVERTINE

ARAGONITE

DOGTOOTH SPAR

The Great Plains and the Mississippi Valley also are covered with sedimentary rocks. These formed during periods when the Gulf of Mexico reached far to the north. The strata, thousands of feet deep, are mostly covered with soil left by glaciers, winds, and rivers.

At the time the Appalachians rose, about 225 to 275 million years ago, they consisted mostly of sedimentary rocks. Most of these have since been eroded away, and a core of harder rocks underneath has been exposed. Some of these are sedimentary strata that became metamorphosed.

Below: Sedimentary strata in Front Range, Colorado—*Edges of hard, up-tilted layers rise as hogbacks above softer strata, which are being eroded away more rapidly. Inset shows erosion pattern.*

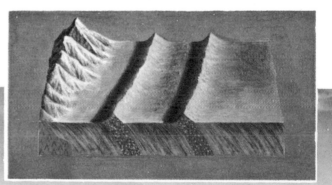

FIBROUS GYPSUM

GYPSUM CRYSTAL

ANHYDRITE

Above: **Minerals from sedimentary rocks—**Halite *(common salt) is found in deposits where salt lakes and seas dried up. Gypsum is deposited by sea water evaporating in dry region. Other minerals shown occur in various forms of limestone.*

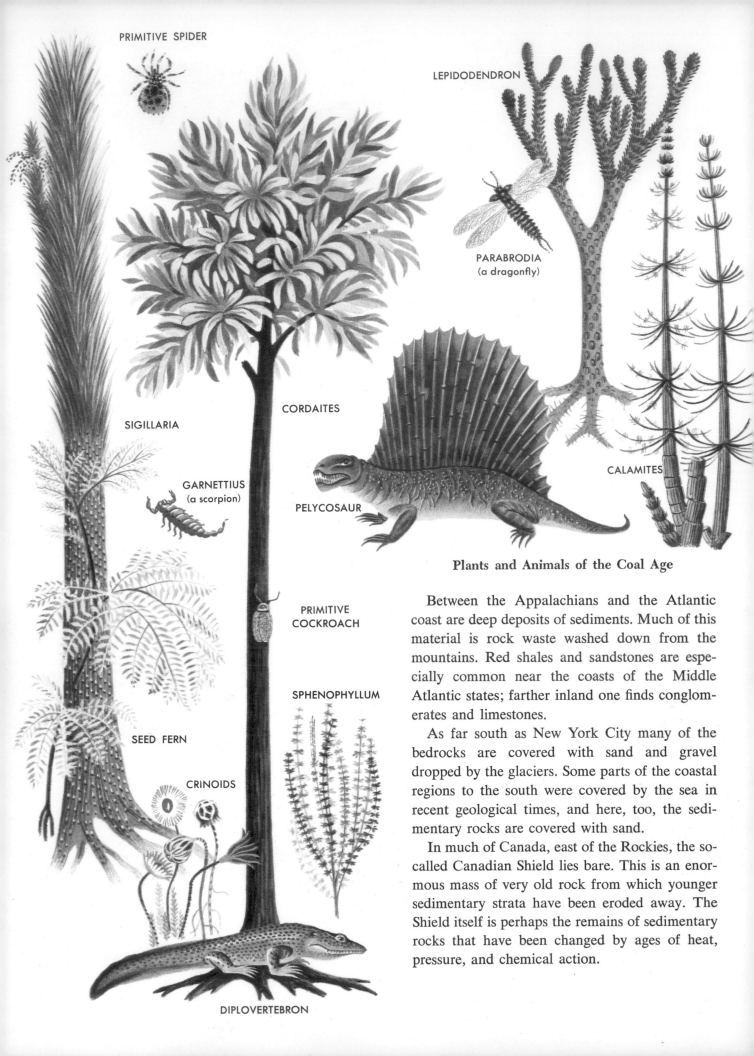

PRIMITIVE SPIDER

LEPIDODENDRON

PARABRODIA
(a dragonfly)

SIGILLARIA

CORDAITES

CALAMITES

GARNETTIUS
(a scorpion)

PELYCOSAUR

PRIMITIVE
COCKROACH

SPHENOPHYLLUM

SEED FERN

CRINOIDS

DIPLOVERTEBRON

Plants and Animals of the Coal Age

Between the Appalachians and the Atlantic coast are deep deposits of sediments. Much of this material is rock waste washed down from the mountains. Red shales and sandstones are especially common near the coasts of the Middle Atlantic states; farther inland one finds conglomerates and limestones.

As far south as New York City many of the bedrocks are covered with sand and gravel dropped by the glaciers. Some parts of the coastal regions to the south were covered by the sea in recent geological times, and here, too, the sedimentary rocks are covered with sand.

In much of Canada, east of the Rockies, the so-called Canadian Shield lies bare. This is an enormous mass of very old rock from which younger sedimentary strata have been eroded away. The Shield itself is perhaps the remains of sedimentary rocks that have been changed by ages of heat, pressure, and chemical action.

SWAMP TREASURE

Heat, pressure, and chemical action change sediments in wonderful ways. Take, for example, the story of a typical coal region.

Some 225 to 275 million years ago, much of the Midwest was covered by long arms of water reaching up from the Gulf of Mexico. In the deeper waters, shales and limestones were laid down. (Mammoth Cave was carved out of some of these limestones.) But in the regions we now call western Pennsylvania and West Virginia, vast swamps developed. Here giant cockroaches, centipedes, and primitive amphibians—some of the earliest land animals—crawled among masses of tall, fernlike plants. Overhead droned clouds of strange, clumsy insects.

The climate was warm, and vegetation in the swamps was thick. Age after age, the primitive plants pushed above the black muck, grew tall, died, and crumpled down into the muck again. Age after age, the dead plant matter piled up.

In time the land began to rise, the sea gradually withdrew, and the swamps began to dry up. For

The Three Principal Varieties of Coal

millions of years clay and sand were washed and blown into the old swamps. The rising of the land went on until the region had become—perhaps 225 million years ago—a part of a majestic mountain range, rivaling the Alps of our time.

High in the mountains, now, were some of the old swamp bottoms. Gigantic forces that had wrinkled the land to form mountains had squeezed the layers of decayed swamp material

"X-ray" view of coal mine—*Vertical shafts are driven down to coal seams, which are then tunneled. Shaft at left is for communication; shaft at right, for ventilation. At left, note "strip-mining" of seam at surface.*

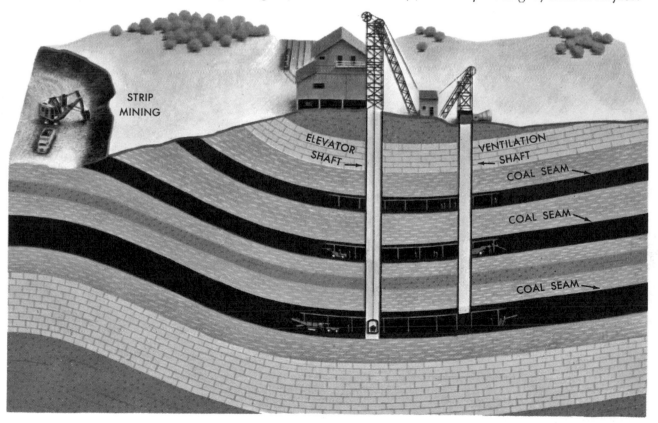

Oil- and Gas-producing Strata

very hard. Where this material had once been hundreds of feet thick, it was now only yards thick. The black, wrinkled, half-folded layers were deep in the mountain rock.

This majestic mountain range—the Appalachians—wore down as millions of years drifted by. Shales and sandstones blanketing the mountains were eroded away. At last, parts of the old, squeezed swamp deposits began to show. They had become the black, rock-like substance we call coal—the fuel and raw material that made so much of our industrial civilization possible.

BLACK GOLD

Petroleum, too, is a treasure we find in the sedimentary rocks. This liquid mineral is the source of our gasoline, heating and lubricating oils, and greases. From it we make a thousand and one articles called plastics and synthetics.

Petroleum comes from the bodies of countless billions of plants and animals whose remains were buried in old ocean bottoms. As sediments piled up and became rock, parts of the remains turned

Strip mining, New Zealand—*Where coal seams are at surface, mining can be done with power shovels.*

112

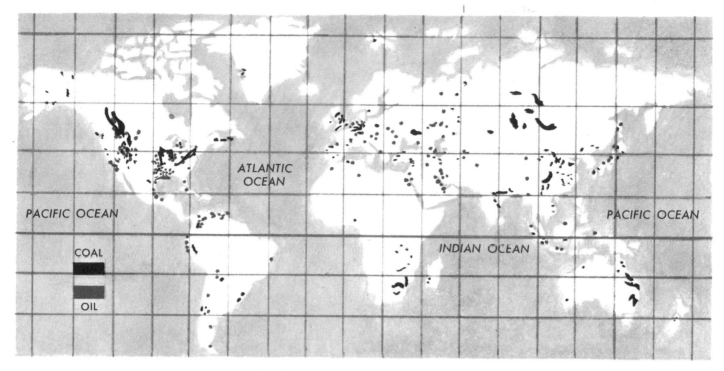

Oil- and Coal-producing Regions of World

into oil and gas, which collected in tiny spaces between rock grains. Then the gas- and oil-bearing rocks were sealed off by strata through which oil and gas could not escape.

Strata containing a great deal of oil have been discovered, some more than a mile down. The deepest oil well, a well in Texas, is over four miles deep. Oil lands include such unlikely-seeming places as the Arabian desert, the plains of Oklahoma, the Gulf of Mexico, and the Sahara.

Is it promising?—*Oil-driller examines sample of rock material brought up from below by core drill.*

Coal-makers—*Plants of coal age were changed to carbon by heat and pressure, but imprints are clear and detailed still.*

Land rising—*Shoreline of San Luis Obispo County, California, displays old wave-cut terrace above present beach. Southern California has wave-cut terraces 1,400 feet above present sea level.*

Lands Rising and Falling

Wherever bedrocks are exposed, we are likely to see the familiar signs of Earth's perennial restlessness—cracking, tilting, squeezing, folding. In mountains, especially, the rocks show signs of a turbulent past.

There are signs, too, of great risings and sinkings of land. Fossils of sea animals in high mountain rock prove that sea bottoms have been lifted miles into the air. Drowned river valleys along seacoasts testify to changes in land level with respect to sea level. Rejuvenated rivers are evidence that land masses worn down by erosion do rise again—not once but many times.

Mostly, these gigantic forces in Earth's crust work very slowly, and man is not aware of them. But they are always at work. Never, even for a moment, is any part of the crust completely still.

LANDS RISING

The rising of lands in some regions has been rapid enough for the inhabitants to notice. For hundreds of years, peoples along the shores of the Baltic Sea, in Finland and Sweden, have seen the level of the sea changing. Old inhabitants remember when some of the small islands were fathoms under water. Farmers whose fields are

114

hundreds of feet above sea level find sea shells scattered through their soil. At some points along the coasts there are wave-cut terraces 900 feet above the sea.

The cause of the rising here is apparently the retreat of the ice sheet that covered the region as recently as 10,000 years ago, when primitive man was still hunting the mammoth and the reindeer over central Europe. As the ice front gradually melted northward, the land was relieved of the tremendous weight of the ice and gradually rose up. It is still rising, at the rate of three to four feet a year, though the ice is now far to the north.

A less rapid rise is occurring in North America from the region of the Great Lakes northward. Old waterlines on northern shores are in places more than 200 feet higher than corresponding water lines on the southern shores. There is a definite upward tilt of the lake bottoms from the south shores northward. Although the ice melted 10,000 years ago, the uplift is still going on.

The coast of California, too, shows signs of elevation. Along the southern shores there are old wave-cut terraces more than 1,400 feet above the sea. Their spacing indicates that this region rose in a series of relatively sudden movements, and by different amounts at different points.

Measurement of the elevation of seashores can be complicated. For instance, the melting of glacier ice during the past 10,000 years has raised sea level by perhaps 200 to 300 feet. On the other hand, there is fossil evidence that *before* the recent ice ages, sea level was over 600 feet higher than now. This great change must be due at least partly to crustal movements.

LANDS SINKING

A century ago, when European geologists were having trouble convincing people that lands do rise and sink, their favorite proof was the ruin of the old Roman market-place at Pozzuoli, in Italy.

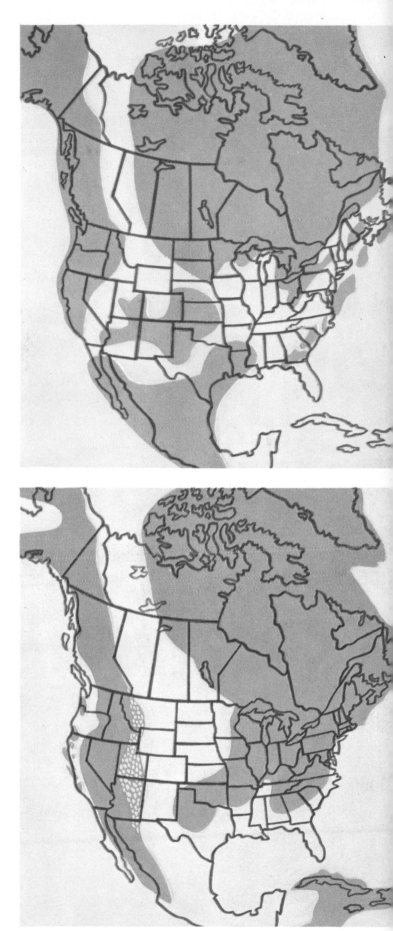

The invading sea—*In periods of subsidence, or sinking, during past periods geologic time, regions of North America have been invaded by sea, then have risen to become dry land again. Upper map shows maximum coverage of continent by sea in Cambrian Period, 450 to 425 million years ago. Lower map shows maximum during Cretaceous time, 100 to 80 million years ago. Speckled area was coastal plain.*

Anticlines and synclines—*Rocks folded into zigzag pattern testify to restlessness of crust. Cliffs on San Juan River, southeast Utah, rise 1,500 feet.*

◄ **Monocline**—*Mt. Timpanogos in Wasatch Range near Salt Lake City, Utah, displays perfect fold. Severe folding is often accompanied by breakage of strata, as indicated here.*

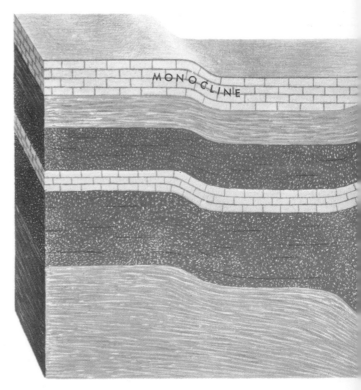

MONOCLINE

Syncline in slate—*Fold is exposed in highway cut, Catskill Mountain region, New York State.*

Here three tall stone columns stand well above the level of the sea, yet they are dotted with holes bored by clams. Apparently after the building was erected the land slowly sank and the columns were partly submerged. For perhaps hundreds of years the clams did their work. Finally the land rose again, and the columns were once more entirely above water.

In North America, land submergence has occurred in recent geologic times along the coast from Maine to the Middle Atlantic States, along the Gulf, and in the region of San Francisco Bay. As the land has sunk, the ocean waters have crept up into the river valleys, forming estuaries.

One of the best-known of these estuaries, or "drowned" river valleys, is that of the Hudson River. Through the sunken valley, salt water has reached up-river 90 miles to the vicinity of Poughkeepsie, New York. East of New York Bay, a shallow channel in the sea bottom connects the mouth of the river with a deep gorge. This gorge,

Types of folds—*Rocks can be folded in countless variations of regular forms shown here. Many folds become sliced off by erosion or distorted in complicated ways by faulting or further folding movements.*

▼

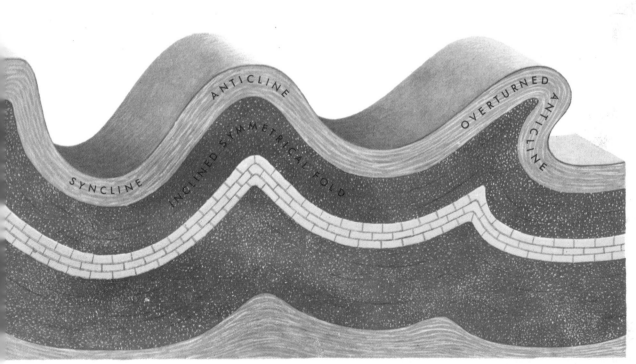

in some places cut 4,000 feet into the continental shelf, reaches eastward about 40 miles. Geologists believe that most if not all of this magnificent submarine canyon was cut by the Hudson when this part of the continental shelf was dry land.

Many sea bottoms show signs of having once been dry land. The sea floor in the vicinity of the Aleutian Islands, for example, is a typical "landscape" of eroded hills and river valleys. Some of this bottom was once a full 1,200 feet higher, with respect to the sea, than it is now.

THE TORTURED ROCKS

Earth's crust is, in some ways, like a mass of stiff taffy. The gravity of Sun and Moon pull at it and make it bulge. Forces inside the planet push and pull on this "taffy" crust from below, and here and there, they squeeze and stretch it. Parts of the crust are flexible enough to bend and even fold under these forces, but other parts break.

Bending forces on a stratum of rock can warp it like a board left out in the sun. Thrusting forces may cause rock strata to buckle upward into folds called anticlines, or downward into folds called synclines. Sometimes the buckling forces continue until folds at the surface break and fall over on to neighboring strata.

Rock does fold. Rock layers being folded deep underground may be squeezed so hard that they cannot break. Instead, the mineral crystals in the

Types of faults—*Faults often occur along with folding. Both are most commonly seen in cliffs and other outcrops. Following pattern of folds and faults across a region is complicated task.*

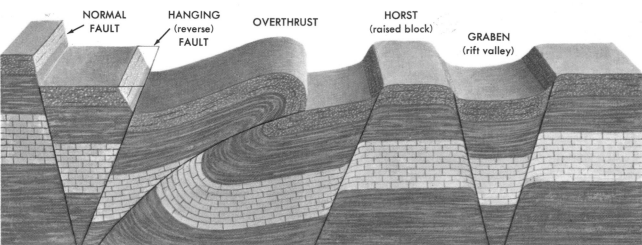

NORMAL FAULT HANGING (reverse) FAULT OVERTHRUST HORST (raised block) GRABEN (rift valley)

MacDonald Lake fault—*Escarpment running diagonally across photo marks very old fault. Surrounding landscape, relatively level, was scoured by ice sheets in recent glacial ages. Escarpment was raised higher more recently.*

rock rearrange themselves as if to relieve the strain; they become metamorphosed.

All bedrocks in time become jointed—that is, cracked or fractured—by underground forces. Blocks of rock formed by networks of joints may rise, sink, or move sidewise. The cracks along which such movements occur are called faults. A cliff formed by the edge of a tilted block is known as a scarp.

Ordinarily, folds and joints are not neat and straight. They are likely to be ragged and irregular, and to occur in various combinations at different places and different times. Tracing them accurately may be a long and complicated task for the geologist.

UP, DOWN, AND SIDEWISE

Folding is the process that has formed most of the great mountain systems. The Rockies and Appalachians, the Alps and the Himalayas—these are folded structures. Along with the folding in such ranges there has been, also, considerable faulting and general breakage.

Faulting alone has raised up mountain ranges. Famous examples in the United States are the Wasatch Mountains in Utah, the Grand Tetons in Wyoming, and the Sierra Nevada in California. In time, erosion may carve up mountain ranges so thoroughly that only an expert can figure out whether it was folding or faulting that made them in the first place.

Valleys, too, can be created by faulting. A chain of such valleys is seen east of the Mediterranean Sea, running from Syria down into East Africa. Most famous is the valley of the Jordan River and the Dead Sea. This very steep-sided valley, nearly 400 miles long and 10 to 25 miles wide, is sunk about a mile below the neighboring region. The fact that this valley is so far below the level of the Mediterranean—2,600 feet—proves that it was

119

Where Earth cracked—*Relief map of eastern Africa and area east of Mediterranean shows system of great rift valleys. (Vertical scale is exaggerated.)*

made not by a river but by the sinking of a block of the earth's crust. Streams can flow into the Dead Sea but not out.

MOVEMENTS SLOW AND SUDDEN

Probably the crust in every region has at some time experienced warping, folding, faulting, fracturing of rock strata, and movements along faults. These processes are continuing, though ordinarily too slowly to notice. The folding that has raised the Himalayas is still going on, for instance, and the ranges are rising faster than they are being worn down. The speed of rising probably is a few inches per year.

Movements along faults are usually sudden but slight—so slight that they may be detected only by such clues as bent or broken well casings and pipelines. Sudden movements of several inches or feet will involve an earthquake.

The so-called earthquake regions of the world are, in fact, regions of "active" faults. The region to the south of the Himalayas has seen disastrous earthquakes in modern times. Another such region lies along the faults that have produced the rift valleys between Syria and East Africa. The western coast of South America, at the foot of the Andes, is very frequently shaken.

Well known in the United States is the strip of land along the so-called San Andreas fault, which begins under the the Pacific floor and runs southeast under the San Francisco area, from which it continues down through southern California into Mexico. Among the many disturbances for which this fault has been responsible in modern times, the great San Francisco earthquake, in 1906, was the most violent. A horizontal movement of 21 feet occurred along the fault. Roads were cut, fences twisted, and property lines upset, much to the disgust of the owners.

THE TANTALIZING "WHY?"

Just about everywhere, the searching eye of the geologist sees the results of movements of the planet's crust. But nowhere does he find a really satisfactory explanation of the forces that keep causing these movements.

The ancients, we remember, believed that the globe's interior was full of fire (which seemed to explain volcanoes), or water (which seemed the reason for springs and rivers), or wind (which might be the cause of earthquakes and volcanic outbursts as well). Underground spirits could always be cited as causes of events that could not be understood otherwise. The reasons for Earth's restlessness were, in fact, so obscure that we can hardly blame the philosophers of the past for guessing wrong about them.

The truth is that although science today is no longer guessing blindly, it is far less certain about the causes of crustal movements than about most other phenomena of geology.

Sinyala fault—*Cleft in Colorado River area near Havasu Creek made valley for river to occupy.*

IS HEAT AN ANSWER?

For a long time most experts believed our planet was once molten. The cooling of the planet seemed to explain the wrinkling of the crust. But today there is scientific doubt as to whether the planet ever *was* molten. Furthermore, calculations have indicated that wrinkling due to cooling would have been too slow to account for the speed of rising in mountain ranges.

Heat, geologists think, *is* part of the answer. It is connected with volcanoes, and perhaps with

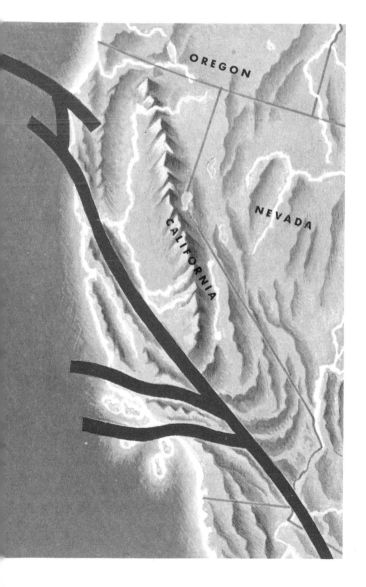

California fault pattern—*Longest of red lines here marks San Andreas fault, at least 600 miles long. This and related faults are continually active.*

121

Scenic jumble—*Garden of Gods in Front Range, Colorado Springs, Colorado, displays sandstone strata up-ended and eroded into hogbacks. Pikes Peak is beyond.*

folding and faulting. The build-up of heat in various parts of the crust could cause expansion and so make the bedrocks fold or crack. Perhaps heated rock in the crust gradually rises as cooler rock sinks, just as warm air from a radiator rises in a room and pushes aside the cooler air, which then sinks toward the floor.

Where might all this heat come from? It is known that the interior of the earth is very hot, and the heat must tend to keep working outward. Some additional heat is created by radioactive minerals in the crust, but not enough, probably, to account for all the heat found there.

EROSION AND BALANCE

Whatever the part played by heat in movements of Earth's crust, erosion also is a cause. A century ago James Hall, an American geologist

who was at the task of tracing out the geological history of North America, pointed out that in some regions the crust becomes severely depressed, or down-bent, by the weight of erosion debris. Estimating the depth of sedimentary rocks in the Appalachian mountains at 40,000 feet, or nearly eight miles, he declared that such thicknesses of sediments could accumulate only if the crust sank steadily as the load increased.

Many years later another American geologist, Clarence Edward Dutton, who had been an assistant to Major John Wesley Powell, built this discovery into his theory of crustal movements. As erosion debris piles up in the hollows of the world, Dutton said, the bottoms of the hollows tend to sink, forming troughs, and the balance between various parts of the crust becomes upset. The sinking of the Gulf of Mexico under the Mis-

122

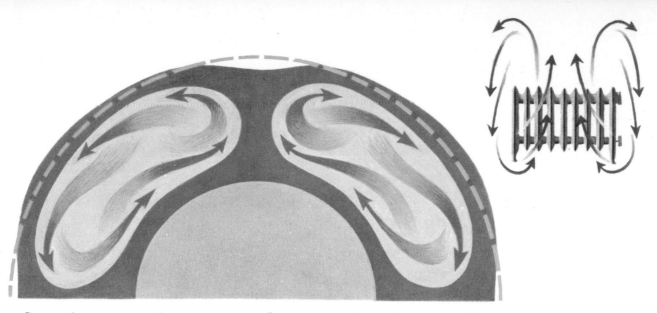

Convection currents—*Temperature-caused movements of mantle material, like movements of air around radiator, may distort Earth's shape and produce folding and faulting. (Distortion is exaggerated here.)*

sissippi delta today is just one example. But, added Dutton, this downward pressure tends to push other material in the crust sideward and upward. In the course of millions of years, a combination of all these movements may be required to keep the crust as a whole in balance. In fact, this is perhaps how mountains rise.

This process described by Dutton is known as "isostasy," from two Greek words meaning "same" and "a standing still." It has strongly in-fluenced the thinking of geologists for over half a century. Yet neither isostasy nor any other theory about crustal movements completely satisfies scientists. Perhaps cooling of the crust, convectional currents, and erosion all play a part. And there may be other causes still unheard of.

Geologists confess that it is the *biggest* questions about Earth that remain unanswered—such questions as how it began, the source of its heat, and causes of crustal movements.

Cause of Crustal Movements?—*Possible isostatic movements of crust are compared here to behavior of wood blocks floating in water.*

Granite rock masses in Earth's crust float in basalt, which is heavier. The higher the masses, the deeper they reach into basalt below.

If tops of highest rock masses are eroded off, and if waste accumulates on neighboring masses, all masses may rise or sink in basalt accordingly.

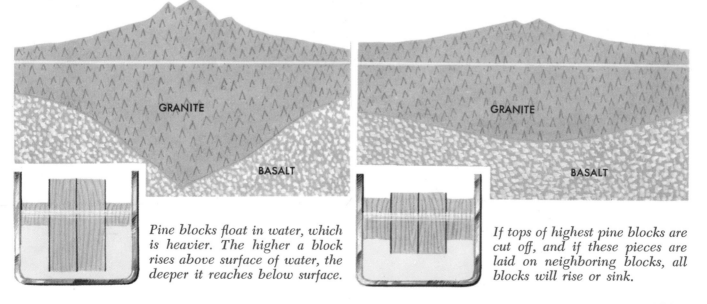

GRANITE

BASALT

GRANITE

BASALT

Pine blocks float in water, which is heavier. The higher a block rises above surface of water, the deeper it reaches below surface.

If tops of highest pine blocks are cut off, and if these pieces are laid on neighboring blocks, all blocks will rise or sink.

From Sea Bottoms to the Clouds

EARTH'S HISTORY is divided into long ages of relative calm and shorter periods of unrest. Underground forces build up in a region for a while and then break loose. For a few million years there is much faulting and folding going on, and perhaps a lot of earthquakes and volcanic activity. Then, so it seems, the underground powers sleep again. Geologists say that the period during which man has risen to dominance on this planet is one of the quieter phases—an age of erosion and land carving, rather than of crustal movements and land elevation.

Periods of crustal movement are perhaps those during which the planet's crust gets itself back into balance after long ages of change. And it is during these periods, apparently, that our new mountain ranges are born.

FOLDS INTO MOUNTAINS

Mountains are basically of four kinds. Some, such as Vesuvius and Mauna Loa, are built up of lava in the form of cones and shields. Others, such as the Wasatch Mountains of Utah, are formed by up and down shifts of blocks of the crust. Some mountains are ruins of high plateaus that have been carved up by rivers: the Beartooths of Montana are examples. But most common of all are the mountain ranges that rise up as the result of gigantic folding movements.

A typical folded mountain range begins as a long, water-filled hollow called a geosyncline. This is a great trough in the crust. It fills with sediments, and its bottom sinks under the weight. The sediments grow thicker and thicker, and the bottom of the geosyncline sinks lower and lower.

High world—*Mountains, which are Earth's noblest scenery, result from slow spasms of crust. View is from Middle Needle, French Alps, near Mont Blanc.*

125

Biography of Appalachians (500 Million Years)

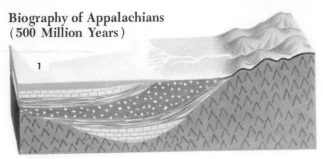

Sediments are laid down in geosyncline, forming strata of shale, sandstone, and limestone. Bottom of geosyncline sinks as weight increases.

Land rises, sea retires, and folding and faulting raise sedimentary strata to form mountains. Networks of streams work to cut down mountains.

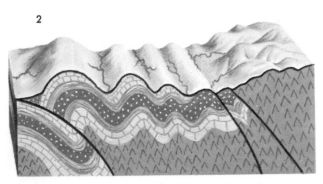

Erosion cuts away tops of folds and reduces region almost to a plain. Having lost grade, streams flow slowly and lack erosive power.

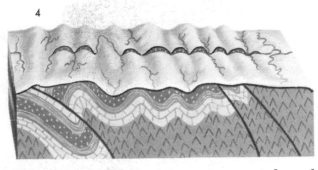

New rising of land gives rivers steeper grade, and new cycle of erosion begins. Erosion pattern mostly follows old folds.

In time, and for reasons that geologists do not fully understand, the region of the geosyncline begins to rise. Gradually the water disappears from the trough, and folds appear along this old sea bottom. The top parts of the folds become mountains, and the bottom parts become what are called the mountain "roots."

The process takes millions of years. While it is going on, erosion keeps grinding away at the mountains, but the speed of rising is greater than the speed of erosion. The mountains may reach heights up to five miles or so before the folding forces wane.

Even after the main process of mountain building is complete, a slight rising may continue. This may be due to the increasing weight of eroded material at the feet of the mountains. The downward push of this material seems to act as an upward push for the mountains.

THE APPALACHIAN STORY

Far back in geologic time, perhaps half a billion years ago, there was a geosyncline—a broad trough perhaps 500 miles wide—running down through what is now eastern North America. For several hundred million years, off and on, this trough was filled by an arm of the sea. Rivers from a big mountain range off the present eastern coast kept pouring sediments into the great central sea. The sediments, up to eight miles thick, built up faster near the eastern shores. Here the shallow sea gradually changed into an area of vast fresh-water swamps—swamps where dead plants piled up to form coal for the distant future. In time, gigantic forces thrusting northwestward caused the geosyncline to bulge upward. Some of the folds were perhaps 15,000 feet high. Folding was so sharp and steep that the original 500-mile-wide syncline was squeezed into a width of only 270 miles in places. Thus, between 200 and 300 million years ago, the Appalachian Mountains were born.

Erosion gradually ground the mountains down. Crustal movements cracked and moved many of the folds. Masses of molten material, granite and basalt, moved up through the breaks in the bedrock. Eventually, the tops of the folds were gone and the mountains were worn down almost level.

126

New uplifts, however, raised the stumps of the old mountains. These stumps, carved by rivers, are the Appalachians we know today.

But what happened to the enormous amounts of rock that were worn off the ancient Appalachians—mountains that in height probably rivaled the modern Alps? That rock was carried away by wind and water, grain by grain, mostly eastward. Vast heaps of the rock waste now lie on the Atlantic coastal regions, forming shales and sandstones up to four miles thick.

MOUNTAINS TO THE WEST

The Rockies make a more complicated story than the Appalachians. They consist of many ranges formed over a large area. This area, the Rocky Mountain geosyncline, reached from the Arctic to southern California and from the present Pacific Coast to Utah and western Arizona.

Some 500 to 600 million years ago, this geosyncline had already formed as a great trough filled by the sea. In the western part, perhaps 500 million years ago, island chains rose, spanning the present regions of Oregon, Washington, and British Columbia. These chains were dotted with volcanoes that spouted lava for millions of years. Volcanic activity, folding, and thrust-faulting gradually raised the islands and made them mountain ranges.

Meanwhile, widespread folding activity in the geosyncline divided it into several troughs. The pile-up of sediments in the westernmost trough 150 to 200 million years ago led to the rise of the Coast Mountains of British Columbia and a range in California. The California range was in the region where, after long erosion, the present Sierra Nevada block rose up.

Sediments kept washing down from the highlands to fill the troughs to the east. In the present area of Nevada and northward, they piled up to depths of eight miles in places. About 100 million years ago folding began in this region, and an-

Veteran range—*Great Smoky Mountains, stumps of once much-higher and more rugged range, are among most ancient in United States. View here is of Newfound Gap, near North Carolina-Tennessee boundary.*

Heaped slabs—*Front Range of Rocky Mountains, near Boulder, Colorado, is topped with sedimentary strata that were raised, tilted, and broken as range formed. Conglomerate "slabs" have resisted erosion.*

other trough developed, still farther to the east. This trough, reaching from the Arctic to the Gulf of Mexico, gradually filled with sediments and volcanic material to depths of four miles. Then millions of years of folding and thrusting movements, lasting on a grand scale until perhaps 50 million years ago, created the Rockies.

Meanwhile, in California, a new hollow had formed and filled with sediments. Folding and faulting there, during the past few million years, have raised the present Coast Ranges of California. The famous San Andreas fault, along which there are still occasional movements, runs through the system of folds and faults in this region.

Some of North America's mountain ranges, such as those that lie buried under the great lava flows of the Columbia Plateau, have been much changed by volcanic activity. All, and especially the older ones, have been much eroded, not only by frost and running water but by the glaciers of the past million years. Here and there, erosion has exposed the mountain cores—great plutons of granite, some perhaps formed by heat and pres-

sure out of old beds of sedimentary rock in the days of active mountain building. Here and there, too, high in the snow-swept slopes, the solid rock yields relics of a quieter past—fossils of trilobites and shellfish, sponges and sea lilies, and other ancient dwellers of the sea.

A CHAOS OF ROCK

For geologists, the Alps are the most tantalizing jigsaw rock puzzle on Earth.

The Alpine region 100 million years ago, in the time of the dinosaurs, was a sea bottom on which sediments were building up. Parts of this old bottom began to rise, perhaps 50 million years ago, to form islands. For 25 million years or so, uplifting and thrusting forces were at work. The foundations of the island chains were pushed up into folds. Then, as thrusting continued, some folds were broken off, were pushed northwestward as much as thirty to forty miles across a smooth "table" of rock beneath, and toppled over.

Still the folding went on, with much breakage of strata as well as severe erosion. Finally, the mountain building phase was over. For perhaps the past 25 million years, the crumpled and broken landscapes have been left to the mercy of frost, glaciers, and running water.

Geologists have spent lifetimes studying the Alps, trying to determine from the wreck of the twisted, jumbled strata exactly what happened. These ranges have been compared to a heap of chunks and slices from an enormous marble cake —a cake that was squeezed and twisted and then sliced in several directions.

MOUNTAINS, VOLCANOES, AND EARTHQUAKES

The great breakage of bedrocks around the edges of the Alps region apparently allowed magma to find its way to the surface and form volcanoes or escape in fissure flows. Earthquakes have been common here in recent geologic time. West of the Rocky Mountains, too, there has been extensive breakage, and here many volcanoes have developed. Earthquakes are common along the Pacific coasts of both North and South America.

Parts of the Himalayas are younger. Much of their rise has occurred during the past million years, and uplift is still going on. Here the rock strata have not been so violently folded. Broken layers have often slid neatly over neighboring layers, sealing the cracks. For this reason, perhaps, magma less easily finds its way to the surface, and volcanoes have not developed. But faulting is severe, and India, south of these towering mountains, has suffered terrific earthquakes.

BLOCK MOUNTAINS

Earth's crust in some places behaves like a broad platform made up of blocks that individually rise, sink, and tilt in response to erosion and forces acting from below. Here and there, a block rises above its neighbors and, by virtue of this elevation, is attacked by the forces of erosion with special vigor. In time the block is carved into individual peaks which we call fault or block mountains. Often the original block is tilted, so that one side of the resulting mountain range has a long, gradual slope, while the other has a steep slope, known as a scarp.

Alpine puzzle—*Block diagrams suggest evolution of Alps in Jura region from geosyncline phase (bottom) to maturity (top). Note overlapping caused by thrust-faulting. While folding and faulting were occurring, erosion was cutting away tops of folds. Final shaping of the Alps has been by glaciation.*

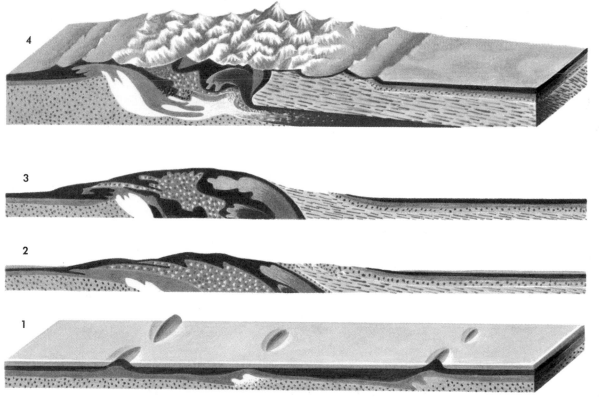

Block mountains—*Sierra Nevada of California, like Grand Tetons of Wyoming, were carved by ice and water out of long, up-raised block, tilted downward toward west. Steep east face of the range appears here.*

A block commonly rises by a series of sudden movements, each adding a few inches—or perhaps as much as 30 to 40 feet—to the elevation. Thus the rise of a range may be rapid. If a movement occurs but once every 50 years, and the gain is only one foot each time, the total rise will be 10,000 feet in 500,000 years. That would be very rapid growth compared to folded mountains.

A famous region of block mountains runs southeastward from southern Oregon through eastern California and Nevada into southwestern Arizona and Mexico. Faulting here has raised dozens of big ranges. Faulting is still going on and earthquakes are frequent.

Biggest of all our block mountain ranges is the Sierra Nevada of California. This began as folded mountains about 150 million years ago, was almost completely eroded away, and then was lifted again by faulting that began about 20 million years ago. The present range consists of a gigantic block nearly 400 miles long and about 75 miles wide. Its eastern scarp rises 13,000 feet above sea level. Its long western slope, buried under sedimentary rocks, is sunk below sea level to a depth of perhaps five miles.

THE MOUNTAIN CHAINS

The main mountain ranges of the world occur in long, broken chains, apparently following lines of weakness in Earth's crust. The regions through which these chains pass are regions of volcanic activity and earthquakes.

The chain running down the west side of the Pacific from Japan to Indonesia is partly covered by the sea. If its base were at sea level, its highest peaks would tower almost as high as Mount Everest. Here have occurred many of the most violent volcanic outbursts and earthquakes of recent times.

An underwater mountain chain winds down the middle of the Atlantic, its highest summits reaching above the waves to form Iceland and the Azores. Volcanic activity is frequent in these islands. In 1957, a new volcanic island burst up out of the sea in the Azores, sank again after 30 days, and soon rose again.

In the Caribbean Sea is a group of islands, the Lesser Antilles, that resemble the volcanic islands of the western Pacific. They rise above the ocean floor as much as 25,000 feet, and are the scene of many volcanic eruptions and earthquakes. Mount

Sculpture of fault block—*Crustal movement raises block (left). Erosion cuts into block (middle), and debris piles up on lowlands below. After millions of years, entire landscape has been reduced almost to plain (right), and debris from original block has been transported elsewhere.*

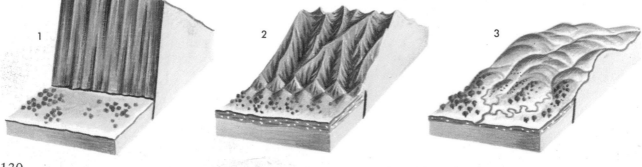

Still building—Izalco Volcano, in El Salvador, here seen erupting at dusk, builds cone higher and higher.

Pelée, on Martinique, is the most notorious peak of this range.

All the mountain chains shown on the map here are young and relatively active. Older, quieter ranges include the Appalachians, the Urals in Russia, the Atlas in North Africa, and the Cape Range in South Africa. All have been much worn down.

One of the earliest known mountain systems once ran diagonally across eastern Canada to Greenland. That was a billion years ago and more. These ranges, the Laurentians, have almost completely eroded away, and only their granite roots are seen now.

Peak of submarine mountain range—*Virgin Islands, in West Indies, like many other island chains, are summits of volcanic mountains that rise miles from ocean floor. Hawaiian Islands had similar origin.*

Lisbon, Portugal, Nov. 1, 1755—Old print tells story of collapsing buildings, fires, and great tsunami that completely wrecked city and took over 10,000 lives. Earthquake at Agadir, Morocco, in 1960 killed 12,000.

When Earth Trembles

MILES DEEP in Earth's crust, gigantic forces are at work. They push and pull; they bend and stretch and squeeze. These are such forces as build mountains. They are more powerful than any forces, natural or man-made, that we see at work on the planet's surface.

In many parts of the world, people rarely if ever have much reason to think about these forces beneath them. But, in other regions, there are sometimes quick and terrible reminders.

Here, the underground forces build up for a time, like steam pressure in a boiler. For months, years, even centuries, they build up. Then, all at once, some weaker part of the underground rock masses reaches its limit of endurance. Under the unbearable stress, it cracks, or fractures, and the release of the stored-up force causes a violent shivering motion in the bedrocks around it. It is this motion, like the vibration of a released bow-string, that we call an earthquake.

At the surface of the earth, the quake may be announced by underground rumblings and reports like distant artillery fire. Then the ground starts moving. The motion may be up and down or side to side, and usually there is some of both. If the land surface is moist sand or clay, lying over the bedrock, it may shake like jelly.

The motions of earthquakes can make boulders dance, knock down people, shake trees out of the ground, and flatten buildings. Cracks may appear in the ground, and the earth on opposite sides may slide in different directions for several yards, twisting buildings out of shape and putting curves in fences, highways, and railroad tracks.

It all may happen in a minute or two—or may continue off and on for weeks.

Ordinary well-constructed buildings can stand a few jolts or slow back-and-forth movements. But earthquake movements are sometimes unbelievably rapid. Buildings are literally shaken to

132

pieces. People are killed or injured by falling roofs and walls. Fires start from cooking stoves, lamps, and broken electrical wiring. Faults break water mains, so that there is no water for fighting the fires as they spread.

Earthquakes also may trigger landslides. Whole villages have been buried by cascades of rock and soil shaken loose from steep slopes. Sometimes a slide blocks the course of a large river through a valley, causing disastrous floods.

Underground forces in a region may be so finely balanced that a thunderstorm or a wind can set off a quake. And one quake may start others.

TOKYO: 1923

One of the worst of all earthquakes was the one that hit the cities of Yokohama and Tokyo, in Japan, a generation ago. These cities lie near the shores of Sagami Bay. On September 1, 1923, the bottom of the bay suddenly sank, and the whole region took a frightful shaking.

A shipmaster out on the bay, who happened to be looking toward the city of Yokohama, saw its buildings bobbing up and down like small boats on rough water. The city was practically shaken to pieces.

Tokyo was not shaken so hard, but fires broke out there as in Yokohama, and water mains snapped. Before the disaster was over, the entire city of Yokohama was a smoking ruin, and half of Tokyo was gone. The damage came to several billion dollars, and 140,000 people died among the falling buildings and the flames.

SAN FRANCISCO: 1906

In the United States the most disastrous earthquake was the one that shook San Francisco in 1906. At five in the morning, when most of the city was still asleep, the tremors began. People on the streets were bowled over. Walls fell out of the sides of buildings. Water mains broke, and the waters flooded through the streets. Fires starting in the buildings could not be checked. The city burned for days, and about 450 people lost their lives.

The San Francisco quake was started by a movement of a big section of land along the San Andreas fault. The land on opposite sides of the fault shifted as much as 21 feet. Minor earthquakes along this fault, with small shifts of the land, are fairly common today.

TSUNAMI, OR "TIDAL WAVES"

An earthquake in a sea bottom has the effect of suddenly lifting or dropping a large volume of sea water. Waves run outward at speeds of 400 to 500 miles per hour. The waves may be only a foot or two high, but they are 100 to 400 miles *long*, and therefore contain far more water than ordinary wind-caused waves. The low height of the wave allows it to pass unnoticed under a ship at sea, unless the ship has special equipment to detect such waves. When the enormous volume of water reaches land, it builds up as a giant breaker —a wall of water high enough to sweep devastatingly over ports and low islands.

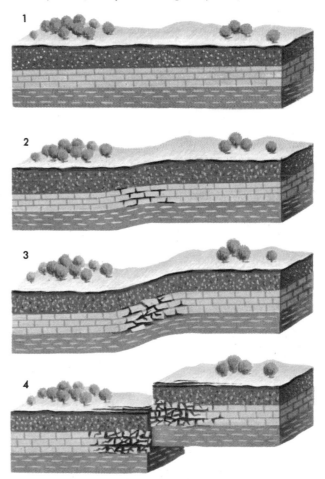

Cause of earthquakes?—*Earthquake occurs probably when rock strata snap, then vibrate before coming to rest in new position. Stage 3 below shows strata just before quake; Stage 4, just after.*

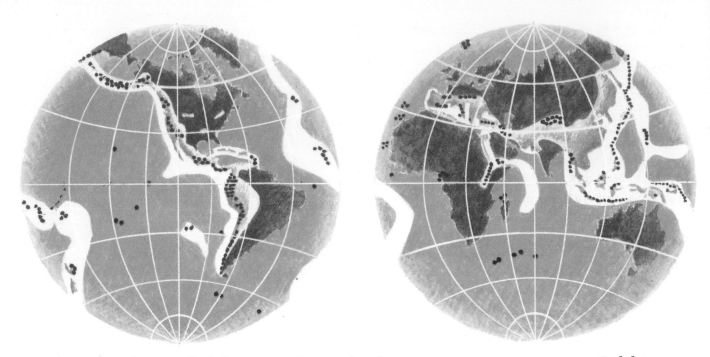

Regions of unrest—Shaded areas are where earthquakes are most frequent or most severe. Red dots indicate centers of volcanic activity. Earthquake and volcanic zones follow lines of weakness in crust.

"Drunken" houses—San Francisco quake shook buildings off foundations, left them at crazy angles.

A great wave of this kind is known as a tsunami. The word is Japanese, meaning "storm wave." Tsunami are also known as "tidal waves," though they have nothing to do with the tides.

Destruction by tsunami has been greatest among islands of the western Pacific, including the Japanese islands and those of Indonesia. When the volcano of Krakatoa blew up in 1883, there was a tremendous earthquake, and the resulting wave was of record proportions. The wall of water that engulfed Java and Sumatra was 75 to 100 feet high, and 30,000 people were swept away.

During an earthquake centered near Lisbon, Portugal, in 1755, a 50-foot wave leveled the lower part of the city. In 1960, a series of earthquakes and tsunami along the coast of Chile caused millions of dollars' worth of damage and the death of several thousand people.

A tsunami can travel thousands of miles. Those that started near the coast of Peru, in South America, during the big quake of 1877 traveled 10,000 miles, reaching Japan in about 21 hours. They were 8 feet high at the end of their journey.

Fortunately, there is advance warning when a tsunami is about to come in. Just as the water along a beach withdraws to join an ordinary wave as it comes plunging in, the water withdraws before the tsunami arrives. But in this case an enormous amount of water retreats. It is as if the tide went from high to low in a minute or two. Then in comes the towering wave.

THE PERENNIAL TERROR

In ancient times, earthquakes even more than volcanic eruptions were events of great terror. Earthquakes were always unexpected, and usually far more destructive. The violent shaking of a city generally meant collapsing stone buildings, fires sweeping the wood or thatch dwellings of the common people, flooding of the city by river or sea waters, and panic as people fled and trampled one another in the streets. Such accounts are common in the Bible, which is the story of peoples in a region that, in modern geologic times, has been especially subject to violent shocks.

Because earthquakes show no outward cause, they remained a mystery to philosophers of old, who attributed them to fire, winds, or waters raging underground—or simply to the wrath of the gods. Our modern understanding of earthquakes has come only with long study of Earth's crust and particularly with world-wide use of an instrument called the seismograph.

AN ALERT WATCHMAN

The seismograph, ingenious yet simple, is built on the pendulum principle. The frame is anchored in the bedrock. One end of the pendulum is attached to the frame, and the other end, which is quite heavy, is free. When an earthquake causes the bedrock to shake, the frame shakes with it. But the free end of the pendulum remains practically motionless.

Also anchored in the bedrock is a rotating spool of photographic paper. Upon the paper falls a steady beam of light coming from the free end of the pendulum. As the spool unrolls, the beam "draws" a continuous line on the paper.

During an earthquake, the bedrock vibrates. So does the spool. But the beam of light, coming from the practically still pendulum, does not shake. Consequently, the line it makes on the paper is wavy, and so the earthquake is recorded. The more severe the earthquake is, the bigger are the waves in the line.

The seismograph is very sensitive. Even when

State Highway 287—*Severe 'quake, August 17, 1959, in Hebgen Lake region, Montana, left broken highway and 5-mile-long, 180-foot-deep lake where Madison River was blocked by 90-million-ton landslide.*

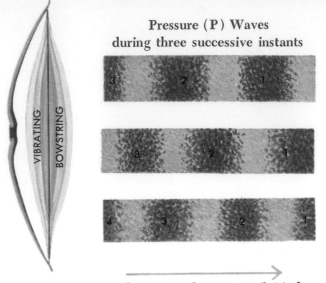

Pressure (P) Waves
during three successive instants

VIBRATING BOWSTRING

P waves suggest vibration of bowstring (left), but they travel as diagrammed here (at right).

Transverse (S) Waves

S waves suggest loop in rope shaken at one end. Diagram shows traveling loops at successive moments.

no real earthquakes are going on, the line drawn by the light beam will be slightly wavy—because of very slight movements in the bedrocks. But let a serious quake occur almost anywhere in the world, and the seismograph is quick to show it.

The epicenter of an earthquake—that is, the location on the crust where the shocks are strongest—can be learned from an analysis of the shock waves. These are of two main types. The primary (P) waves travel through bedrock like ripples across the surface of a pond. The secondary (S) waves move like loops along a rope shaken at

Seismograph principle—*Rotating spool, anchored in bedrock, vibrates during quake. Light beam from motionless pendulum makes photo record on spool.*

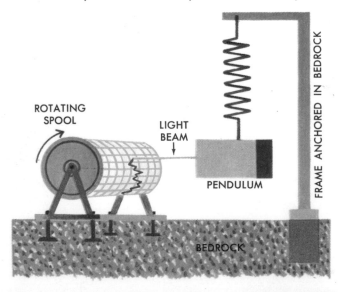

ROTATING SPOOL

LIGHT BEAM

PENDULUM

FRAME ANCHORED IN BEDROCK

BEDROCK

one end. P waves travel at 5 miles per second, and S waves at 3 miles per second. When an earthquake occurs, the P waves always reach the seismograph first. The distance from the epicenter to the seismograph, in miles, is equal to one half the number of seconds between the arrival times of the different waves. Thus, if a seismograph records P and S waves arriving 200 seconds apart, the epicenter is about 100 miles away.

Seismograph stations in many parts of the world are on the alert twenty-four hours a day. Stations check with one another whenever unusual shocks are detected. As shown in the accompanying diagram, the geographic location of the epicenter can be determined from the reports

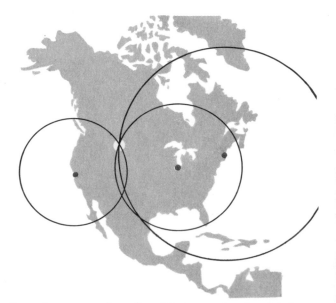

Locating an earthquake—*Distance of epicenter from each of three stations is determined. With this distance as radius, circle is drawn around each station. Epicenter is about at point where circles meet.*

of three or more stations. Sometimes a severe earthquake, and its location, are announced to the world hours or days before the news arrives from the stricken region.

Seismographs show that Earth's crust is constantly in motion. There are, on the average, several thousand earthquakes per day. Most are so slight that they can be detected only by seismographs. But about twenty-five quakes each year are big enough to do serious damage.

Most earthquakes start from faults 40 miles or less below the earth's surface. Some occur at depths up to 100 miles, and very few at depths of 400 miles or so. The very deepest ones occur only in the western Pacific region, where mountain building is now rapid and volcanic activity is constant. Quakes at depths of 100 miles or so sometimes occur in the Lesser Antilles, in the Caribbean.

EXPLORING BY SEISMOGRAPH

By means of seismographs, scientists have been able not only to keep track of earthquakes but to learn much about the interior of our planet.

Some earthquake waves, like sound waves, pass through different kinds of bedrock—shale and basalt, for example—at different speeds. Also, they change their direction as they pass from one kind of material to the next. Thus waves from the same quake will travel outward at uneven speeds and along crooked paths. When they reach seismographs at various locations on Earth's crust, their times of arrival, directions, and other characteristics will be clues to the rock structures through which they have traveled. In this way our planet can be "explored" to depths of hundreds or even thousands of miles.

Small, artificial earthquakes are created for the practical purpose of locating oil deposits. In

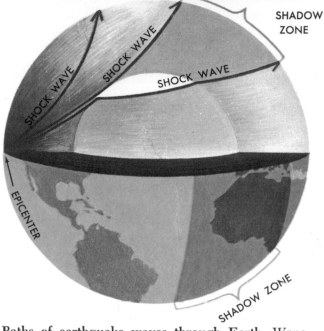

Paths of earthquake waves through Earth—Wave travels at different speeds through different materials. Its direction changes (it is refracted) as it passes from one material to another. Shadow zone is area where, because of refraction, no shocks are received.

an area where oil is thought to exist, small explosions are set off at various points, and records made by seismographs placed nearby are analyzed. The records give clues to the nature of the rock strata below, their order and depth, their tilt, and the likelihood that they contain oil.

Oil prospecting, modern style—*Blast set off at each shot point creates seismic waves, which are reflected differently from different strata. Reflected waves received by detectors are recorded electrically in truck. Comparison of records indicates whether strata are likely to have oil deposits. Surveyors find more clues in surface contours.*

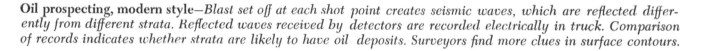

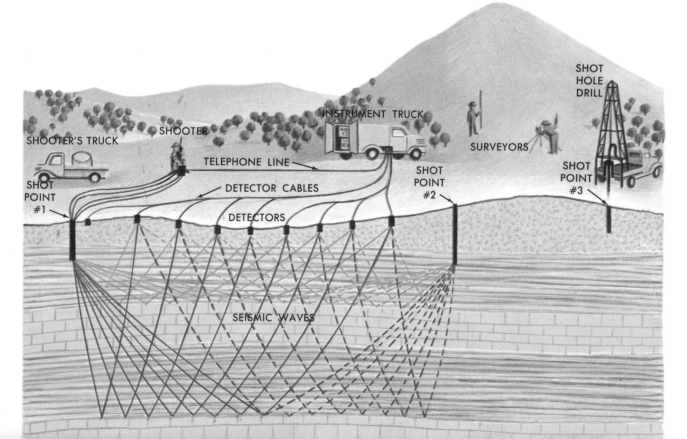

The Changed Rocks

TITANIC FORCES fold, squeeze, rub, bend and stretch the rocks of our planet. Magma boiling up from the depths runs through the joints. Mineral-bearing water and gases, cold and hot, percolate through the cracks and between the rock grains.

Is it any wonder that rocks change? They do change, and almost too greatly to believe. The process is called metamorphosis (a Greek word meaning "change"). Changed rocks are called metamorphic rocks.

A PUZZLE SOLVED

Metamorphic rocks have long been a problem for geologists. These rocks have formed in ways not fully understood from igneous and sedimentary formations. They may be encountered at any stage of their development, which may be simple or highly complicated and may occur over a period of a few hours or a few hundred million years. It is quite understandable that in the conflict between Neptunists and Plutonists, after 1800, both sides were confused about this type of rock.

James Hutton had been excited to find sedimentary strata sharply folded, greatly compressed, and apparently changed in their essential nature. He supposed rightly that much of the rock of our planet had become altered with time. In the mid-1800's Sir Charles Lyell, roving the British Isles, Europe, and America, putting together for the first time a history of Earth's past, confirmed him. Sir William Logan, the great Canadian geologist, later showed that the foundation of North America—exposed today in the Canadian Shield—is a great core of metamorphic rocks.

The formation of these rocks is, however, essentially a matter of chemistry—of minerals changing into different minerals, of substances becoming

"Rock of Ages"—*Quarry has been blasted 350 feet down into Vermont granite. Long considered igneous, granite formations like this may be old sedimentary rocks changed by heat, pressure, and infiltration.*

transformed in their basic natures. And so the puzzle of metamorphism was not one that the geologist in the field could solve alone. For much of our modern understanding of the process, we must thank the chemical laboratory and the atomic physicist.

THE STORY OF A GARNET

A good example of metamorphism is the process by which garnets often form. Garnets are crystals of a very hard, reddish mineral likely to be seen in certain kinds of rock outcrops or in rock debris.

Imagine a great river carrying bits of clay down to its delta. Gradually, in the delta, layers of clay harden into shales. The delta sinks, but eventually rises to become dry land, a folded mountain.

The folding puts the shale under great strains. Gradually the mineral grains line up at right angles to the pressure. They form slate—the kind we use for garden walks and pavements.

"Slickensides"—*Smoothly grooved face of gneiss resulted from movement of bedrock along fault. Such crustal forces are great enough to change rocks not only mechanically but chemically.*

SHALE

GARNET

SLATE

Biography of garnet—*Beginning with shale (top), creation of garnet can be traced clockwise through stages. Erosion and chemical change could finally reduce garnet to clay and start cycle anew.*

PHYLLITE

GNEISS

SCHIST

The pressure continues. The slate becomes the rather shiny rock phyllite. Still greater pressure and heat change the phyllite into schist, a flaky rock that may include much mica. Under further pressure, the schist turns into gneiss.

Gneiss, a rock with large crystals, has a streaked or "flowing" appearance. It contains a wide assortment of minerals, sometimes including garnets choice enough to be valued as semiprecious.

It takes only a few paragraphs to tell this story. But the chemistry is complicated, and the garnets

"Stacked blackboards"—*Tilted slate in Catskills, New York state, was once layers of clay on delta.*

you pick up in a quarry or on the roadside may have been a billion years in the making.

THE MAGIC OF HEAT AND PRESSURE

The process by which a lump of clay can become a garnet is only a sample of what is happening in the bedrocks beneath our feet every day. Limestone is changing into marble, a harder stone with big crystals. Volcanic dust is being transformed, like clay, into phyllite and mica schist. Gray basalt is being turned into greenstone. Here and there, in deep-down places, carbon is being changed into diamonds.

The quartz grains of sandstone are tough. They can stand terrific pressures and heat without changing. Yet the rock as a whole can be changed.

GRAY SLATE

RED SLATE

Rock-changing intrusion—Limestones near Franklin, N. J., have been much metamorphosed by magma intrusions such as the one that made this dike.

Water may trickle through it, leaving minerals that cement the quartz grains together. Then when the rock is broken, it will break not between the grains but through them. The sandstone has become quartzite.

In a conglomerate under pressure, quartz pebbles may become lengthened and flattened. The material of the quartz crystals seems to move from places of higher pressure to places of lower pressure and form new crystals there. The same process may occur when granite turns into gneiss.

Coal shows dramatically what heat and pressure can do. Underground plant remains may change into simple soft coal, which burns easily because it contains certain gases. But where coal is found in rock strata that have been sharply folded, as in western Pennsylvania, these gases are not present. Pressure from folding has formed a new kind of coal: anthracite. Where pressure has been extreme, the anthracite—a hard, long-burning coal—has become graphite. Graphite is fine for pencil leads, but it will not burn.

MAGMA AS A ROCK CHANGER

Magma coming up from the depths is terrifically hot. This boiling mess of minerals-to-be presses against other rocks, and parts of these melt and mix with the magma.

Magma can melt only the rocks near it. But its heat may travel a long way through bedrocks, helping pressure to change them. Rock near the magma and changed by it forms what is called an aureole around it. Where a dike or a sill can be identified in a formation, an aureole can be looked for also.

WANDERING ATOMS

Different types of rocks that are simply held against one another may, over a long enough period, change in their chemical natures. For rocks, like all other substances, are made of the very tiny particles that we call atoms. Even though rock

Metamorphic assortment—Here are only a few of the many kinds of rocks and minerals that may result from heat, pressure, and infiltration.

BLACK MARBLE

QUARTZITE

WHITE MARBLE

CHLORITE SCHIST

QUARTZ SCHIST

HORNBLENDE SCHIST

HORNFELS

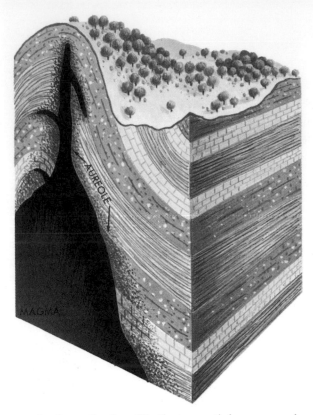

Metamorphic zone—*Wherever magma forces its way up through a rock series, some metamorphism results. Heat, pressure, and infiltrating material from magma cause chemical changes. Zone of changed rock around magma is called contact aureole.*

Metamorphic rock is remarkable but not at all uncommon. The so-called "shield," or core, of each of the continents, is metamorphic. Huge sections of such rock are exposed where mountain ranges, such as parts of the Rockies and Appalachians, have been deeply eroded.

GRANITE: A QUESTION MARK

"Wandering atoms," plus heat and pressure, may explain the nature of the rock we call granite.

A common theory has been that Earth was originally molten. Some scientists have said that at this time granite, being lighter than basalt, separated from it and floated to the top. This granite eventually cooled in big blocks which became the continents. Since then, the blocks have become partly covered with sedimentary rocks and have been invaded here and there by new molten matter—granite and basalt—from below.

Today many geologists have come to doubt that the granite of the continental blocks is original

may look perfectly still, these particles are racing round in it at great speeds. Occasionally a particle gets loose and shoots into the neighboring rock, where it may join other racing particles. In time, such wandering atoms may form new clusters of minerals.

Cores of the continents—*Shields, with adjoining platforms, are apparently exposed cores of the continents. Platforms are shield areas covered by sedimentary strata.*

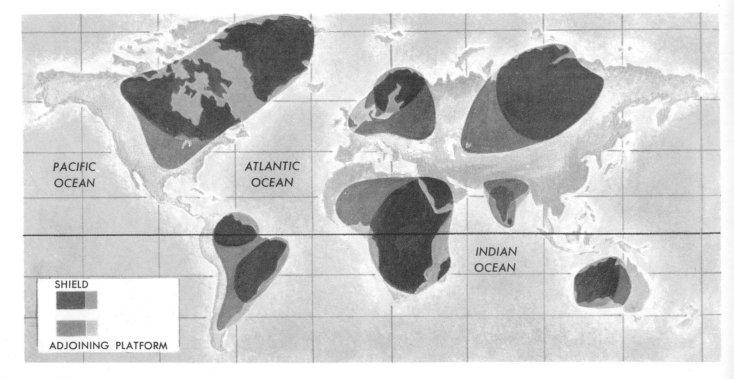

rock of the planet. In some mountain ranges they have discovered granite completely surrounded by sedimentary rocks, with no sign that the granite came from elsewhere and pushed any of the sedimentary rock aside. In some places, surely, granite is nothing other than a changed sedimentary formation. Possibly *all* granite is old, changed sedimentary rock. And if that is true, the continental blocks themselves were once sedimentary rocks.

Earth's crust was, perhaps, originally basalt, entirely covered by the sea. Troughs in the basalt filled with sediments, which may have become rock and may have been invaded and changed by magma from below. Folding and faulting then raised these changed formations to become islands —our planet's first dry lands — and eventually mountain ranges.

The cores of these mountain ranges, meanwhile, were subjected to great heat and pressure. Materials from the depths kept working up through them. At last the old cores became granite. As erosion destroyed the mountain ranges, the cores were exposed and worn down to low levels. The continental blocks were thus formed.

This process was completed—so the argument runs—perhaps three billion years ago. Since then, slow folding of the continental blocks has continued, sediments have filled the troughs, mountains have risen, new granite cores have formed, and erosion again has set to work on the ranges.

All this is, of course, theory—not history definitely known. Granite remains one of the great problems of geology. When we know more about its origin, we shall know much more about these continents we live on.

Changed rock?—*Stone Mountain, near Atlanta, Georgia, is granite "monadnock" remaining after erosion of softer surrounding rocks. Once it may have been core of much larger mountain.*

FRANKLINITE
(in Calcite)

**ZINC
ORES**

SMITHSONITE

SPHALERITE

ZINCITE, WILLEMITE,
and FRANKLINITE

EARTHY HEMATITE

**IRON
ORES**

HEMATITE
(oolitic)

HEMATITE
(specular)

METEORITE

MAGNETITE

SMOKY QUARTZ

APATITE CRYSTALS IN CALCITE

ROSE QUARTZ

EMERALD

CASSITERITE
(Tin ore)

GALENA
(Lead)

FLUORITE
(twin crystals)

The Making
of Minerals

MINERALS are what rocks are made of. Minerals are substances formed by natural processes out of what are called the basic elements—iron, copper, oxygen, sulfur, and the ninety others. Some rocks consist almost entirely of one kind of mineral; thus sandstone is mostly quartz. Other rocks, such as gneiss, may contain scores of minerals in different proportions.

From the time he first began using rocks for axes, knives, and spearheads, man has been making use of minerals. Odd, attractive minerals such as agate, obsidian, and garnet must have been used by primitive man for ornaments and charms long before written history began. Simple processes for getting copper out of rock were developed more than five thousand years ago. Since then, the growth of civilization has depended very importantly on advances in the science of getting minerals out of Earth's crust and processing them for human use.

Readers of this book know that there is nothing "magic" about minerals—nothing we cannot understand. Minerals are natural parts of the natural world. Chemists and mineralogists know how most minerals form, how they will behave under

AUGITE   JADEITE

COPPER ORES

NATIVE COPPER

CHALCOPYRITE

AZURITE

MALACHITE

BAUXITE
(Aluminum ore)

STAR SAPPHIRE

DIAMOND

HORNBLENDE

EMERY
(Corundum)

certain conditions, and how different minerals may react with one another. We have, let us say, a scientific understanding of these materials of our planet.

MINERALS AND IMAGINATION

This modern knowledge of minerals has been slowly, painfully gained. Although man was quick to put minerals to practical use, his ideas about them were for long (and still are) entangled with superstitions. The understanding of minerals, as distinguished from practical use, has come but recently.

Aristotle explained the rocks as created by the light of Sun and stars—an explanation that satisfied most scholars for fifteen centuries. In the Middle Ages a few thinkers, groping for a better explanation, guessed that minerals grew from seeds. Some said that a sort of juice, working its way through Earth's crust, was the producer of minerals. Other minerals were produced in the bodies of animals and plants—or grew out of water—or fell from the sky. One group of scholars taught that minerals were male and female, having their families underground. Still others

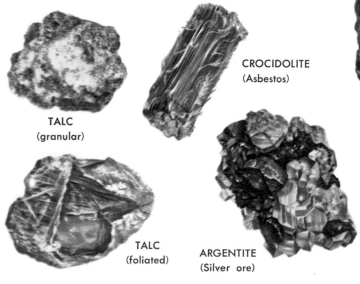

TALC
(granular)

CROCIDOLITE
(Asbestos)

AGATE
(rough)

AGATE
(shaped)

TALC
(foliated)

ARGENTITE
(Silver ore)

GOLD ORE

GOLD
(in Quartz
with Pyrite)

145

MICROCLINE
(Feldspar)

LABRADORITE
(Feldspar)

SULFUR

SERPENTINE

RUBY

ORTHOCLASE
(Feldspar)

ANORTHITE
(Feldspar)

ANORTHITE
(Feldspar)

ALBITE
(Feldspar)

SKUTTERUDITE
(Cobalt ore)

MUSCOVITE
(Mica)

BIOTITE
(Mica)

COBALTITE
(Cobalt ore)

GRAPHITE

believed that certain minerals, as proved by mysterious "writings" on them, were fashioned by subterranean spirits.

In the Middle Ages there was little interest in learning about the natural properties of minerals. Scholars were properly interested in philosophy and religion; God had made the world and that was that. Experiments with minerals were left to the alchemists—dirty, secretive men puttering around their crucibles and ovens with the dream of transforming lead into gold. The so-called educated man's knowledge of minerals was little more than a collection of superstitions.

Minerals conceal their natures rather well. Forget the textbooks: try to imagine that common salt consists of a yellowish gas and a silvery-looking metal! If you believe your own eyes alone, do diamonds and charcoal really consist of the same element—carbon? In fact, still forgetting twentieth-century books, you could not clearly distinguish between minerals and other things,

such as cherry pits and fossils, sugar and bone. It is little wonder that people of a few centuries ago, believing in magic and having no notion of the chemical make-up of our world, told themselves fairy tales.

SOME OBVIOUS GUESSES

There is reason in the odd old beliefs. The sight of stalactites and stalagmites in caves logically suggests that rocks and minerals are formed from underground juices. A tree growing with its roots around a rock is credited with giving birth to it. Pebbles swallowed by animals to aid in digestion, and gallstones and other hard materials formed in the human body—these might seem to prove that plants and animals make stones.

A large crystal of quartz with several smaller crystals attached may be their "parent." Some stones *have* fallen from the sky: meteorites. And who but underground spirits could be responsible for the surpassing beauty of diamonds, the decorative banding in marble and gneiss, the deep blackness of obsidian, the "writings" in agate?

Minerals of strange appearance or properties stimulated the imagination. A stone fallen from the sky probably was dropped by the heavenly powers. A piece of hematite of reddish hue would be a good bet for curing blood diseases. Onyx, because of its "cold, opaque" appearance, must cause hate and evil visions.

Some minerals had feelings, like people. Do not iron and lodestone strongly attract each other? Nearly all minerals, in fact, had active powers for good or evil, or were symbols of things important to man.

Today, in the twentieth century, some of these superstitions are still with us.

A NEW LOOK AT MINERALS

Minerals began to be regarded primarily as natural materials in the sixteenth century—a time when men were eagerly exploring not only the globe but the heavens, the air, and the earth beneath. First to take the new viewpoint was a German named Georg Bauer, better known as Agricola because most scholars in those times went under Latin names. Agricola himself wrote in Latin, as European scholars had been doing for fifteen centuries.

Agricola was a mining expert in Saxony, where flourishing industries had grown up to make the most of the rich mineral deposits. Busy at the job of getting ores out of the ground and of processing them quickly and cheaply, Agricola had to brush aside old superstitions and build up a store of information that could be depended upon. His book *De Re Metallica,* published in 1556, summing up his experience, classified minerals not as to their magical properties and uses but in ways that could help in identifying them, mining them, and making them useful. Agricola wrote of color and weight, transparency and luster, taste and odor, shape and texture—all good, solid terms. He noticed typical forms, such as those of quartz crystals, as well as hardness, com-

bustibility, brittleness, and cleavage. He spoke scornfully of those who wrote learnedly about magical powers in gems.

Agricola grouped the kinds of rocks in which minerals occur. Some of his classifications sound odd today, but they reveal his determination to see things as they really are. He is justly called the father of mineralogy.

Agricola's system of classifying minerals was like the classification of animals and plants according to their outward forms. But minerals are

Metallurgy in Germany, 16th century—*Illustration in Agricola's* De Re Metallica *indicates processing of ores was highly developed, despite lack of science in modern sense.*

chemical substances obviously quite different from organisms. The next necessary step was to study them as to their crystal forms and chemical make-up. The great German mineralogist Abraham Gottlob Werner, leader of the Neptunists against the Plutonists, recognized these possibilities, but stuck to the old system mainly. It was a Frenchman, René-Just Haüy, who founded the science of crystallography, and a Swedish chemist, Jöns Jacob Berzelius, who worked out basic methods for the chemical analysis of minerals. Scientists of the late nineteenth and twentieth centuries went on to explain minerals in terms of atomic physics.

WHAT MINERALS ARE

Minerals are made of combinations of chemical elements. The chemical elements are made of atoms. And the atoms are made up of combinations of tiny electrical particles—particles so tiny that there are billions in a pinhead.

In all, there are about a hundred chemical elements, but many are quite rare. In various combinations, these elements form between 1,500 and 2,000 kinds of minerals.

Most minerals are combinations of just a few elements. Ice (which is a mineral) has oxygen and hydrogen, and quartz consists of silicon and

Open-pit mining—*Enormous hole marks site of open-pit copper mine in Chile. In open-pit mines in Mesabi Range, Minnesota, and in Quebec Province, Canada, soft hematite iron ore is dug out with power shovels.*

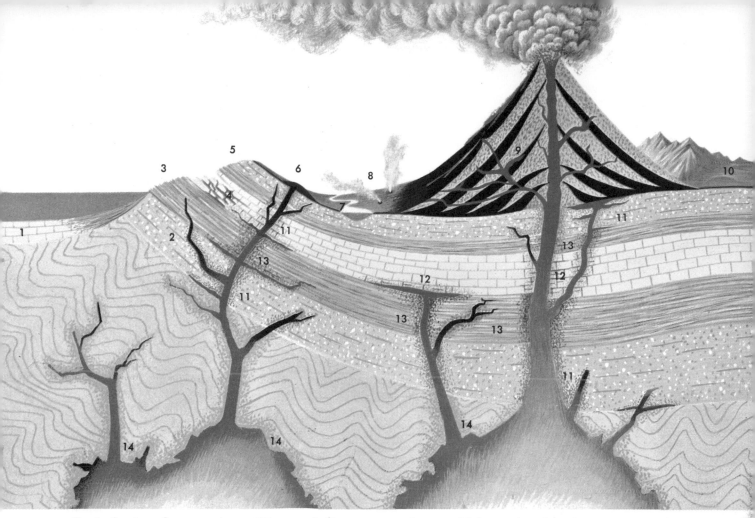

Typical mineral occurrences—*Diagram indicates some sites at which certain minerals may occur:*

1 *Sea bottom:* calcite. 2 *Ore vein:* galena, sphalerite, chalcopyrite, pyrite, arsenopyrite, etc. 3 *Weathered shale:* kaolin, bauxite, other clay minerals. 4 *Limestone caves:* calcite, dolomite, gypsum. 5 *Weathered sandstone:* quartz. 6 *Weathered ore vein:* azurite, malachite, cuprite, anglesite, smithsonite, chrysocolla, cerussite. 7 *River valley:* placer deposits (gold, platinum, diamond, cassiterite, magnetite, ilmenite, garnet, zircon, monazite, rutile). 8 *Fumarole, geyser, and hot spring:* sulfur, hema tite, geyserite, gypsum, opal, zeolites. 9 *Igneous rocks:* feldspars, quartz, olivine, pyroxene, hornblende, magnetite, biotite. 10 *Desert playa:* evaporation salts (common salt, potassium and magnesium salts, gypsum, borates). 11 *Metamorphosed sandstone:* quartz, feldspar, mica. 12 *Metamorphosed limestone:* calcite, dolomite, wollastonite, tremolite, diopside. 13 *Metamorphosed shale:* garnet, mica, quartz, feldspar. 14 *Contact zone:* garnet, epidote, pyroxene, hornblende, sulfides.

oxygen. Calcite (making up most of the rock limestone) combines the metal calcium with carbon and oxygen. Carnotite, a mineral from which the element uranium is obtained, has five elements: potassium, uranium, oxygen, vanadium, hydrogen.

Just how all the elements originally formed, at the time the solar system was created, is not known. No one can say why there are about a hundred elements instead of a thousand. But we do know how many of the minerals have formed in the past and are forming today.

MINERALS FROM MAGMA

Some of these substances are formed by magma rising from the hot depths of the planet. As this molten stuff comes up, it contains the mate rials that will become minerals. Which ones will form depends on temperature conditions and the particular combinations of materials in the magma. Thus the magma coming up into the volcano of Mauna Loa will form basalt rock, with typical minerals that make up basalt; but the magma of Pelée forms rock more like granite.

As magma cools, minerals form in it. Some form first as gases, then turn to liquids as the magma continues cooling, and finally become solid. As the cooling process goes on, all the magma, or nearly all of it, gradually takes some kind of solid form.

The rock formed in this way may consist of tiny grains that look very much alike. Or the rock may have streaks of different kinds of minerals. It

149

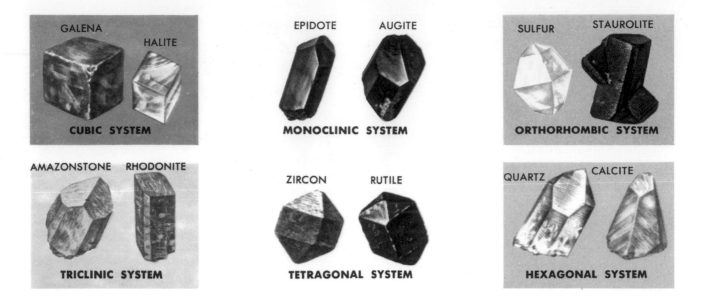

all depends on what the magma had in it and the conditions under which it cooled.

If magma cools slowly, it ordinarily makes larger mineral crystals than faster-cooling magma does. Slow cooling gives crystals time to grow large before hardening is complete.

Usually, magmas that cool very deep do so slowly and thus tend to form large crystals. Some slow-forming crystals have grown to the size of a house. But magmas cooling near the surface harden faster and may form crystals so small that we need a microscope to see them. Lava pouring out of a volcano may cool so fast that crystals do not have time to form at all; the lava hardens into a smooth, glassy mass such as obsidian.

MINERALS FROM OTHER SOURCES

Magma may change the nature of rocks that it touches on the way up. Magma flowing against sandstone, for example, may cause large quartz crystals to form in it. Heat from magma may produce crystals of mica and garnet in shale, and a large variety of minerals in a limestone, especially if this is impure.

Minerals result from the action of water, also. Ground water that dissolves calcium carbonate out of limestone may later deposit it in the form of clear, glassy-looking calcite—stalactites and stalagmites in caves. Billions of tiny particles of sodium chloride—we know it as table salt—are dissolved out of the land by running water, then carried for a while and dropped when the water evaporates. That was how big salt deposits in New York state and in the Gulf of Mexico formed.

MINERAL CHARACTERISTICS

Minerals come in all colors of the rainbow. One kind may turn up in different places with different colors. Quartz, for example, appears in white, rose, and other hues. Rose quartz gets its color from a tiny amount of iron oxide in it.

Each mineral has a certain way of cracking and splitting. Some split into flat sheets, as mica does. Some, such as calcite, break into neat blocks. Flint and many other minerals break like glass, leaving curved surfaces. Magnetite is one of many that show a grainy surface where they break.

The way each mineral reflects light—that is, its luster—is another characteristic. Precious stones are famous for their luster, but rock salt is not.

Hardness and heaviness are still other traits. Diamonds are by far the hardest of natural min-

erals; bauxite is relatively soft. Magnetite, which is rich in iron, is quite heavy and is magnetic. A small group of minerals, such as uraninite and carnotite, are radioactive.

Most minerals when they cool from the molten state, or when they are left by evaporating water, form crystals. Crystals are exact, often beautiful forms that depend on the nature of the mineral itself. The arrangement of the atoms in the molecules that make up a substance determines the shape of the crystals that will form. Ice crystals, determined by the physical nature of common water, are among the most beautiful of all.

Crystals of many common substances, such as sugar and salt, can be prepared by dissolving a small quantity in water and then evaporating the water. Seen under a microscope, they are unexpectedly interesting.

COLLECTING ROCKS AND MINERALS

Walks, hikes, and vacation trips are the more interesting if one can recognize rocks and minerals. Tens of thousands of people now make a hobby of identifying, collecting, and even cutting and polishing them.

The main kinds of rocks, such as granite, basalt, and shale, are fairly easy to recognize after a little practice. Some minerals can be quickly learned, too, and the forms in which they appear in rocks can be fascinating.

Specimens can be looked for wherever bedrocks are exposed; for example, in road cuts,

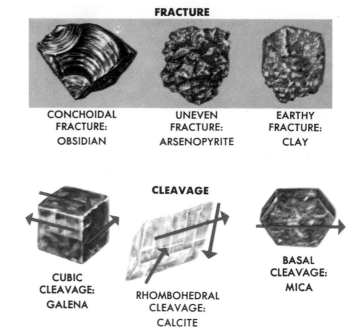

FRACTURE

CONCHOIDAL FRACTURE: OBSIDIAN

UNEVEN FRACTURE: ARSENOPYRITE

EARTHY FRACTURE: CLAY

CLEAVAGE

CUBIC CLEAVAGE: GALENA

RHOMBOHEDRAL CLEAVAGE: CALCITE

BASAL CLEAVAGE: MICA

quarries, mines, steep hillsides, and excavations. Streambeds, beaches, glacial moraines, desert areas, and volcanic regions also are likely places. In some localities most of the bedrocks may look monotonously the same, but wherever the strata have been sharply folded or invaded by magma, interesting specimens may be found. Minerals are likely to occur also where trickles of ground water have deposited them; for instance, quartz crystals in limestone joints.

Certain minerals cannot be identified even by experts without laboratory tests. But, with a guide book to help, anyone can soon learn to identify scores of specimens. The effort is fun.

Equipment for rock collector—*No equipment is vital, but geologist's hammer, bag for carrying specimens, and storage rack or box help greatly. Other items can be obtained as collection grows.*

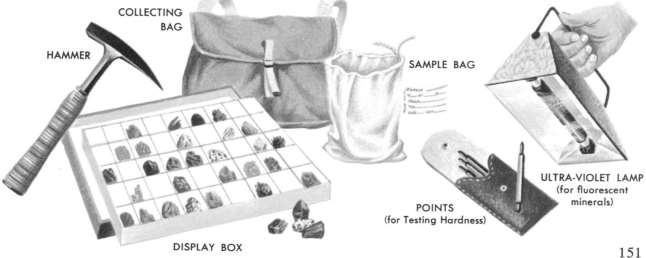

HAMMER

COLLECTING BAG

SAMPLE BAG

DISPLAY BOX

POINTS (for Testing Hardness)

ULTRA-VIOLET LAMP (for fluorescent minerals)

Wandering Poles—and Continents?

EARTH HAS BEEN called a giant magnet, and so it is. As our planet rotates, like the armature of an electric motor, it produces around itself a magnetic field of force. All science students have seen the experiment in which the magnetic field around a bar magnet is outlined clearly when iron filings are sprinkled over the magnet. Similar magnetic lines of force reach outward from Earth.

During the International Geophysical Year, the United States government performed an experiment, "Project Argus," which demonstrated the pattern of magnetic force around our globe. An atomic bomb was exploded 300 miles above the South Atlantic. By means of high-altitude rockets the radioactive content of the atmosphere over many parts of the globe was then checked. Within an hour, it was learned, the particles of radioactive dust from the explosion spread out and, under the

influence of the Earth's magnetic field, enveloped the planet.

LODESTONE AND COMPASS

The magnetic compass, by which mariners could find their way over unknown seas, was in use in the Middle Ages, but our modern understanding of Earth's magnetism began in 1600. In that year the English physician William Gilbert, called by some the father of electricity, reported on some interesting experiments done with a sphere of lodestone—a magnetic mineral better known today as magnetite. When he hung a magnetized needle by the middle over the lodestone, one end of the needle would always swing around so as to point toward the same spot on the lodestone, and it would also dip toward that point. These were exactly the phenomena observed by

1903, the northern magnetic pole has traveled several hundred miles northward. It is now at 76° north latitude, 102° west longitude.

WHY TERRESTRIAL MAGNETISM?

Terrestrial magnetism is easily tested at Earth's surface or out in space by artificial satellites, but it is the interior of our planet that holds the secret of how this force is created. The interior beyond a depth of a few miles is for all practical purposes about as inaccessible as the planet Jupiter. So the geophysicist in search of causes must get his information mainly from surface observations and from man-made magnetic phenomena.

Terrestrial magnetism is, we know, an aspect of the force that Newton called gravitation. Every object exerts a push or pull on another object in proportion to its mass, or amount of matter it contains, and in inverse proportion to its distance from the other object. Earth's rotation produces the pattern of magnetic forces which Project

seafarers with their compasses. Lodestone, Gilbert showed, acts very much like Earth. Probably Earth, too, is a magnet.

Long ago, however, mariners learned—sometimes to their dismay—that their compass needle did not point exactly toward the Earth's geographic north pole, or pole of rotation. It pointed toward a location between Greenland and Alaska. Navigators had to allow for this "error" in reading their compasses.

But that is not all. Compass error varies by many degrees from region to region. Observations must be made all over the globe to learn what the error is at each location, and tables of this information are constantly used by navigators everywhere.

For some 400 years now, scientists have been observing and recording these magnetic phenomena. As a result still another fact about terrestrial magnetism has become apparent: the magnetic poles themselves are wandering! Since the year

Earth's magnetic field—*Iron filings dropped on bar magnet produce similar pattern. Note difference between magnetic and geographic poles on Earth.*

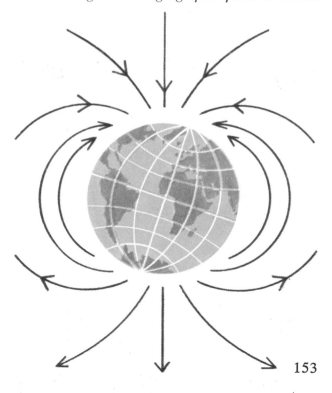

iron is several hundred times stronger. Yet terrestrial magnetism is strong enough to have some peculiar and interesting effects beyond what it does to a compass needle.

For one thing, there is the odd phenomenon we call the aurora, or northern and southern lights. The aurora is the glow of gases high in Earth's atmosphere—hydrogen, oxygen, nitrogen. When atoms of these gases are hit by high-speed particles ejected by explosions on the Sun, they glow like the gas in fluorescent bulbs. As the solar bullets come racing into Earth's magnetic field, they follow curving paths according to the lines of magnetic force. Thus we have the familiar and beautiful auroral patterns, such as "curtains," "rays," and "crowns."

The auroras are brightest over the magnetic poles, where terrestrial magnetism is strongest. When there is a display over one pole, there is a simultaneous display over the other one, too. An observer on a satellite, a few thousand miles out, might sometimes see twin auroras over the north and south poles, like giant fluorescent fountains.

BILLIONS OF TELL-TALE MAGNETS

Terrestrial magnetism becomes a clue in one of the most interesting detective stories of geology. This story begins with certain minerals, particularly hematite and magnetite, which are compounds of oxygen and iron. These substances commonly form in basalt magma when it cools within the crust or emerges as lava. In the cooling process, the grains become magnetized: each becomes like a tiny bar magnet. At the time it forms, the material around it may be quite fluid, so that the grain is able to swing one way or the other and, like a tiny compass needle, line itself up with Earth's magnetic poles. Then it "freezes" in this position. Enough magnetic grains become lined up in this way so that a geophysicist, testing the volcanic rock carefully, can tell from their positions the direction of the magnetic poles.

Now, these tiny compass needles do not lose their magnetism like a toy magnet that is tossed into a drawer and forgotten. In rocks known to

Argus demonstrated. The shifting of magnetic poles may result from changes in the Earth's axis of rotation—changes which, in turn, could be caused by changes in the balance between masses of material within the planet. Indeed, some geophysicists say the hot plastic material between the Earth's crust and its hard core may slowly circulate, like currents of warm and cool air in a room. Such convectional currents, just possibly, could upset Earth's interior balance occasionally and disturb its evenness of rotation. Motions of these currents might also explain differences in magnetic deviation from place to place.

A peculiar fact is that, through the years, there is a westward drift of Earth's magnetic field. The reason could be an inconsistency between the speed of rotation of Earth's mantle (the part just below the crust) and the speed of rotation of the crust itself. If the mantle is rotating eastward more slowly than the crust is rotating eastward, then the net effect is an apparent westward drift of the mantle. This could have important effects in terrestrial magnetism.

EXPLAINING THE AURORAS

Even where it is strongest, at the poles, Earth's magnetic force is actually very weak. The pull exerted by a toy horseshoe magnet on a piece of

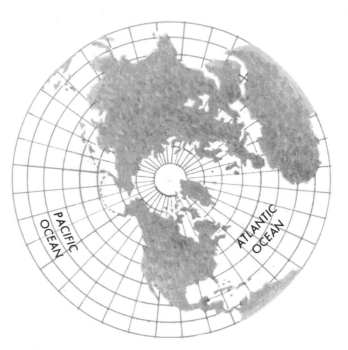

be millions of years old, the tell-tale grains are present, with their magnetism unchanged. Even grains that are by turns eroded out of the original volcanic rock, washed or blown across the Earth, and buried under thousands of feet of sediments keep their magnetic properties. As such traveling grains drift to the bottom of a lake or sea, many are free to swing and find the north-and-south position. This position is held as the sediments become rock.

Grains of magnetic material found in both igneous and sedimentary rock formations in North America, Great Britain, and Australia indicate that the magnetic poles have wandered far and wide through the ages. The north magnetic pole apparently has been located in such places as the North Pacific Ocean, Korea, and Arizona. But that is not all. At times in history, the north and south magnetic poles have exchanged places!

The magnetic poles, we have noticed, are not identical with the geographic poles. Yet scientists believe it is the rotation of Earth that mainly determines its pattern of magnetism. So if the magnetic poles have wandered, probably the geographic poles, too, have wandered.

Are the little compasses playing tricks on us? That is unlikely, for other kinds of evidence hint that they are quite reliable. Ancient glacial debris of the Permian Period has been found within about 700 miles of the equator in Africa. Rock "needles" dating from this period, around 300 million years ago, point toward a region in the northwest Pacific Ocean at a latitude of 42°, or about the latitude of New York. If the north pole actually was there during the Permian, then the south pole was in the South Atlantic, and Africa was probably much nearer the pole than it is now. That might account for glaciers in the heart of Africa during the Permian Period. And pole wandering might account, too, for such odd discoveries as coal strata (produced by warm-climate swamps) in Spitsbergen and Antarctica.

Magnetic keys to past?—*Lonely sandstone knoll, Zion National Park, Utah, is of rock type that may yield clues to former positions of Earth's poles.*

Take another example: Recently, geophysicists examined sandstones formed around 300 million years ago in Wyoming and Utah from wind-blown sands. The shapes of the rock formations indicated the direction from which the prevailing winds came during that ancient age: northeast. According to modern weather knowledge, the direction of the prevailing winds in an area usually depends rather directly upon the latitude of the area—its

Spitsbergen: a balmy land—*Spitsbergen, on Arctic Circle, has big coal deposits, seen here in cliffs beyond coal workings (foreground). Coal-producing swamps could have flourished only in warm climate. Difference between climate then and now may be due to pole wandering.*

distance from the equator. Judging from the sandstones in Wyoming and Utah, the weather expert would suspect that the geographic north pole at that time was somewhat north of the present location of Japan.

And what do the magnetic needles in these sandstones suggest? The same.

WANDERING CONTINENTS, TOO?

Polar wandering, it appears, may have been matched by the wandering of continents.

The possibility that great land masses have moved about through the ages was suggested by Sir Francis Bacon, back in the seventeenth century, when he noticed that the coastlines of South Africa and South America roughly "fit." Were these two bodies of land once a single land mass?

In the twentieth century a number of scientists, especially Alfred Wegener in Germany, began to

push this theory. They attempted to show that not only South Africa and South America, but other continents also, are fragments of larger ancient land masses. Most scientists have considered the crust too rigid to allow any wandering of continents. But clues offered by magnetic rock needles now make continental drift sound more reasonable. Movements of continents would explain certain puzzling inconsistencies in Earth's magnetic history.

Small land masses are even now shifting with respect to each other—for example, the San Andreas fault in California. If small masses can shift, perhaps big ones can, too. Great rifts discovered

Birth of continents?—*Maps show three stages in formation of continents from original land mass, according to continental-drift theory. Dotted lines indicate where land blocks might have broken apart.*

1

156

in the ocean bottoms—in the Mid-Atlantic Ridge, for example—may be significant. The crust of Earth may not be so rigid after all.

A TUMBLING EARTH

What scenes rise up in our imaginations! Greenland a land of palms . . . southern Africa ravaged by great ice sheets . . . the north pole near Japan . . . steaming swamps in Spitsbergen . . . whole continents breaking up . . . a planet rotating at times like a jittery top!

These are matters that need careful observation and study. But right now there is little doubt that old Earth has from time to time got out of balance inside, has begun to wobble, and has recovered a smoother motion only by changing its axis of rotation.

What gigantic forces could have disturbed our planet? A tremendous meteor, like the ones that blasted out Meteor Crater in Arizona and the Ungava Crater in Quebec, Canada? Shifts of the planet's ice caps due to changes in the amount of heat received from the Sun? Or shifts of material inside the Earth, due to convectional currents?

Perhaps the cause was heavy accumulations of sediments in certain regions—or whatever else causes the stresses and strains that keep some lands rising as mountains and others sinking to become sea bottoms.

Anyway, causes which existed in the past probably exist now, and one of these days Earth may be rolling over again. The motion is likely, of course, to be extremely slow. Probably it is happening now.

2

3

157

Seascapes

THE SEA IS still one of our planet's little-known domains. It covers over two thirds of Earth's surface; it is shallow indeed compared to the diameter of Earth. Yet what lies beneath the waves is still only sketchily known. Only recently has deep-sea exploration begun to tell the facts about the ocean bottoms and the events that have happened down there through the ages.

SOUNDING THE DEPTHS

In the days when sea depths were measured by means of a rope or wire with a weight on the end, tossed overboard from the ship, a skipper could know whether he had enough water under his keel. Charts could be prepared to keep ships off the shoals and reefs along the sea highway. But sounding of this sort revealed little about the real nature of the bottoms. Today sounding is done by means of an automatic, continuously

working machine which sends compression waves (like sound waves in air) down through the water, records the length of time it takes for the wave to bounce back from the bottom, and (since the speed · of sound through salt water is known) translates this information into a reading of the depth. A ship zigzagging over a region of ocean can determine the contours of the bottom nearly as accurately as contours are measured by skilled surveyors on land.

Another favorite instrument of oceanographers is the corer, which consists essentially of a piece of pipe and a weight at the end of a long cable. Dropped to the bottom, the pipe sinks down into the sediments, and a sample of these sediments, called the core, enters the pipe, which is then pulled up. The sediments can also be sampled by means of a "grab," which is a bucket-like device that is dragged over the sea floor.

Atlantic bottom—*Artist's drawing, based on map made from soundings, shows diverse topography: continental shelves with canyons, ocean floor, deeps, submarine mountains, and Mid-Atlantic Ridge with great rift.*

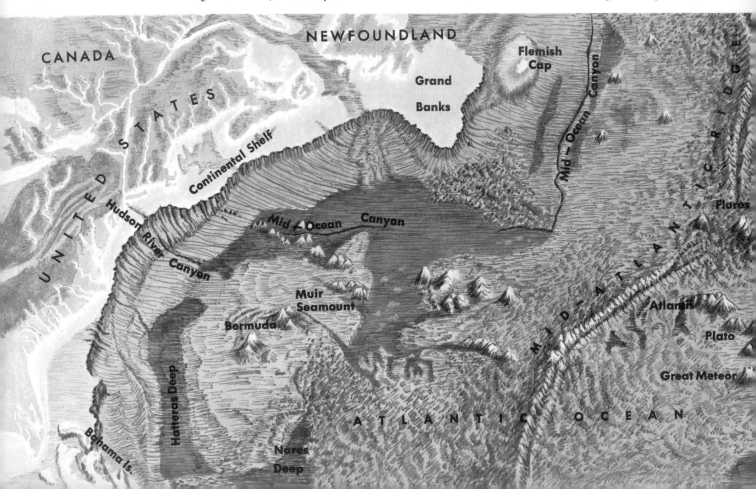

In recent years geologists, like sportsmen, have turned also to underwater breathing devices. With these, geologists can explore the bottoms to depths as great as 300 feet.

Special thermometers are used for measuring the temperature of water at various depths. Changing temperatures are clues to the sizes and directions of ocean currents, and to living conditions for ocean life. The speeds of currents also are measured. Closed cylinders are lowered to any desired depth, opened to allow a sample of water to enter, then closed again and raised to the surface, where scientists can test the water for its saltiness, density, and content of living organisms. Bathyscaphes are lowered to depths of miles, where scientists can view and photograph the bottom life.

Explosions can be set off at the surface and the shock waves, rebounding from strata in the ocean bottom, can be recorded. The pattern of these "echoes" gives hints as to the depth of sediments on the bottom, the kinds of rock strata and their thicknesses, and their inclination. The principle is the same as in seismic oil prospecting, described earlier in this book. In fact, such prospecting is now being done along the continental shelves.

The unknown sea—*Old print reflects fear of sea due to ignorance. True nature of sea bottoms, as areas with features comparable to land (see below, left), has become known only in 20th century.*

THE OCEAN FRONTIER

Science is making the study of the ocean bottoms a serious business. Ocean depths and bottom contours are important to the study of ocean currents, which in turn are important—as in the case of the Gulf Stream and the Japan Current—to world climates, to shipping and fisheries. A knowledge of ocean depths, currents, and temperatures is vital to naval forces.

Sediments on the ocean bottoms, accumulated for millions of years and less disturbed than sediments on the continents, can supply missing pieces to the jigsaw puzzle of Earth's past. The ocean bottoms must hold evidence as to whether the continents have ever really drifted, and there may be clues to past—and perhaps future—glacial ages. In sea sediments lie the remains of prehistoric animals and plants that could help us to trace the travels of species from region to region long ago. The crust beneath the sediments may help to explain processes that cause mountain building and earthquakes.

Geologists are interested in the kinds of animals that are brought up from the deeps. Back in the last century, it was thought that the deeps might be the home of some creatures "left over" from the very ancient geologic past, but for a long time no such specimens were discovered. Recently, however, the appearance of several Coelacanths, which date from the Devonian Period, over 300 million years ago, has aroused new interest. Oceanographers will be keeping a sharp eye on what the traps bring up.

Continental Shelf
FRANCE
PORTUGAL
SPAIN
Antiolfair
Madeira
Canary Is.
AFRICA

Sounding—*Depth is indicated by time required for sound to reach bottom and return to sounding device.*

ALONG THE CONTINENTAL EDGES

Once the oceans were thought to lie in nearly flat basins. Today it is known, on the contrary, that the seascapes are in many ways quite like landscapes, with their mountains and valleys, plains and plateaus and canyons, volcanoes and "rivers"—that is, swift bottom currents.

The continental shelves have long been familiar to mariners and landlubbers. These broad, gently sloping platforms, running out from the shores to depths usually of about 600 feet, have an average slope of some 20 feet per mile. At the outer edge the slope steepens abruptly and, at the rate of 150 to 300 feet per mile, falls to the ocean floor. The floor averages around 12,400 feet in depth, compared to the average elevation of 2,700 feet for the land.

The continents have been compared to blocks, roughly beveled along their ragged upper edges, set upon the ocean bottoms. But this comparison is not very accurate, as we shall see.

SUBMARINE CANYONS

The continental slopes are laced here and there with gorges, or submarine canyons, some of them as large as the Grand Canyon. The Hudson Gorge, running out from the mouth of the Hudson River, at New York City, is 200 miles long, and at its deepest point is more than two miles below sea level. A similar giant submarine canyon has formed off the mouth of Africa's Congo River. A smaller one, much explored by oceanographers, is near La Jolla, California.

Exactly how such gorges have been cut is not definitely known. It is certain that the upper parts were once above sea level and were being cut by rivers or by valley glaciers. During the recent glacial periods, a large amount of Earth's water was locked in glaciers and ice caps, and the ocean levels were 250 to 300 feet lower than today. An evidence of the recent rise of ocean levels is the fiords in the coasts of northern lands.

Coring—*Canadian scientist on* HMS Oshawa *lowers core to get sediments from bottom for analysis.*

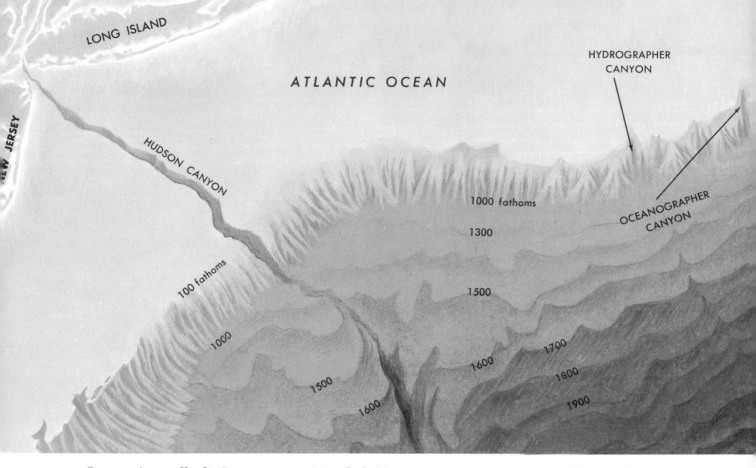

LONG ISLAND

ATLANTIC OCEAN

HYDROGRAPHER CANYON

NEW JERSEY

HUDSON CANYON

OCEANOGRAPHER CANYON

1000 fathoms

1300

1500

100 fathoms

1000

1600

1700

1500

1800

1600

1900

Once a river valley?—*Canyon in continental shelf runs far out from present mouth of Hudson River. Portion of canyon near New York City may have been river valley in glacial ages, when sea level was much lower than now. Deeper part of canyon may have been cut by turbidity currents.*

What, then, of the lower parts of the gorges, which were thousands of feet below the level of the continents? The answer apparently lies in what geologists call turbidity currents. These are currents loaded with sediments and dissolved materials. Some, moving down slopes as great as 400 feet per mile, have a cutting power hundreds of times as great as the swiftest streams on land.

UNDERSEA MOUNTAINS

Much of the ocean floor is fairly level or gently rolling, but here and there, like the land, it has become rumpled into mountain ranges, sunk to great depths, raised into plateaus, cut with valleys, broken by faults, and even cracked to allow the escape of molten material from the depths.

Running down beneath the Atlantic Ocean, almost from pole to pole, is the zigzagging Mid-Atlantic Ridge, its loftiest peaks barely rising above the waves to form scattered islands, as the Azores and Canaries. It has great ravines, saddles, and cliffs like any mountain range on the continents. It also has a long rift, which may account for the many earthquakes recorded in the vicinity. Most of the Ridge rises about 10,000 feet above the ocean floor and is less than a mile beneath the waves. In the South Atlantic, it is connected by the great Walfisch Ridge to the western shore of Africa. Another mountain arc forms the Lesser Antilles in the Caribbean Sea; the notorious Mount Pelée is in this system.

The Pacific Ocean, too, has its giant submarine mountain chains. In the mid-Pacific one of them rises three miles to the ocean surface to form the Hawaiian Islands. Similar ranges form the Aleutians, the Kuriles, the islands of Japan, the Philippines, and the East Indies. These Pacific ranges are the world's most active earthquake regions. Many of the peaks have been volcanic in modern times—Mauna Loa, Mount Mayon in the Philippines, fateful Krakatoa in the East Indies, and Katmai in Southern Alaska.

161

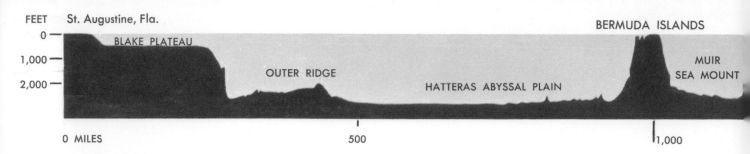

FEET — St. Augustine, Fla.
0 —
BLAKE PLATEAU
1,000 —
OUTER RIDGE
2,000 —
HATTERAS ABYSSAL PLAIN
BERMUDA ISLANDS
MUIR SEA MOUNT

0 MILES   500   1,000

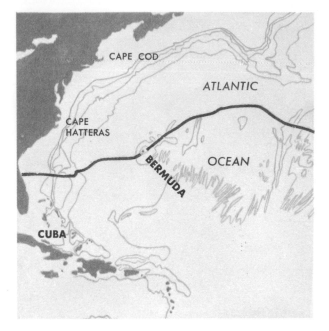

CAPE COD

ATLANTIC

CAPE HATTERAS

BERMUDA

OCEAN

CUBA

Atlantic profile—Depth sounding reveals continuous variation in depths between Florida and Mid-Atlantic Ridge. Line on map (left) shows course of ship which made soundings. (Vertical exaggeration is 40 to 1.)

the northern waters, which would then have less ice on them. Less ice could mean increased evaporation from the ocean surface and, therefore, heavier snowfalls, growth of the ice cap, and a new glacial age for the northern hemisphere.

CORAL REEFS

In the warmer waters of the world, many oceanic islands as well as shallows along the edges of the continents are fringed with deposits of coral. These deposits are the hard, sharp-edged, limy remains of countless billions of little sea animals. Some coral reefs have built up in a ring-like form around islands, along the shore. Where an island has sunk beneath the waves, or a rise in the ocean level has covered it, the corals have kept building and thus have created an atoll—a ring of coral around a lagoon instead of an island. Elsewhere we find huge barrier reefs far offshore, such as the Great Barrier Reef of Australia, 1,200 miles long.

Reef-builders are generally active from a little above low-tide level to a depth of about 150 feet. But where the ocean level has risen since the corals began work, the bottom of the reef may be much deeper—at times several hundred feet down. Widths of coral reefs range from a few yards to nearly a mile. The home of many types of ocean life, and a highly interesting realm for skin divers, coral reefs have been the graveyard for many a storm-tossed ship.

Undersea mountains show many of the forms we see on land. The ranges are cut by ravines and valleys—perhaps partly the work of turbidity currents. Here and there relatively low, flat-topped single mountains called sea mounts rise above the floor. And there are the extinct volcanoes, called guyots, with tops that appear to have been sliced off by the waves.

Some oceanographers think a ridge in the North Atlantic had something to do with the recent ice ages. This ridge acts as a barrier to warm ocean currents moving toward polar waters. A lowering of the ridge would allow the currents to warm

DEEPS AND TRENCHES

The ocean floor falls away into low basins, called deeps, 23,000 feet and more beneath the

Land created by sea animals—Coral atoll lies in South Pacific, between islands of Aitutaki and Tahiti.

waves. These are long, wide troughs of a size and shape similar to those of the great river valleys of the world—the Mississippi, the Danube, the Amazon. Perhaps turbidity currents account for some of these troughs.

Deepest of all are the great trenches, which are located always next to the great submarine mountain arcs. Some of the deepest and longest are those near the Marianas Islands, the Philippines, the Aleutians, and the Lesser Antilles. Recently the bottom of the Marianas trench, at 37,800 feet, was reached by two men in a bathyscaphe.

These V-shaped trenches, only five miles or so wide at the bottom, may run thousands of miles through the ocean floor, and some reach depths of more than six miles. One of the greatest of the trenches, reaching 2,000 miles along the west coast of South America in the shadow of the Andes, is 40,000 feet, or nearly eight miles, below the Andean summits.

It is as if the trenches had been dug into the ocean floor to provide material for piling up the nearby mountains; and this, in a way, is perhaps what has happened. Around these mountains and trenches the Earth is extremely restless; here is the site of the most deep-seated, the most violent, earthquakes. This is where sudden heavings of the ocean floor create great tsunamis. A large proportion of the volcanoes of the present geological age have burst forth near the Pacific trenches.

CONTINENTS FROM OCEAN BOTTOMS?

Some geologists believe that what is happening in these dark depths, six and seven miles down, may help to explain how the continents themselves came to be. Cooled parts of Earth's crust in the ocean deeps (where the temperature is always near freezing) may be sinking, dragging adjoining rocks down with them, and thus forming the trenches. A trench may fill with sediments, which

gradually harden into rock. Then, because this sedimentary rock is lighter than the material in the surrounding crust, it may start rising above the ocean floor, just as a block of wood, pushed under water, will rise again. If the rise continues long enough, it may produce a mountain range, which in turn may become a chain of islands. And a continuing series of such events may at last produce a continent.

If that is how the continents did form, why is the foundation rock of the continents granite? We recall that most geologists once believed granite was part of an original molten crust of Earth— that it collected into blocks which floated on the heavier basalt, and thus formed the continents. Now it is thought that the granite may have been created out of a combination of basalt and sediments from the original sea floor, mixed with other minerals that worked up from deeper down, and transformed by heat and pressure. Perhaps the continents formed in this way several billion

Science afloat — *Lamont Geological Observatory's* Vema, *like other such vessels, is equipped for such work as depth-sounding, coring, water analysis, surveys of marine life, and mapping of currents.*

years ago and have remained essentially the same, except for the occasional sinkings which have allowed the sea to invade the land and leave layers of sedimentary rock, like chapters of Earth history, for today's geologist to read.

THE MOHOLE

For years scientists have been tantalized by the mystery of Earth's mantle. The mantle is the material that lies between the crust and the outer core. Studies of earthquake waves indicate that it is much denser than the crust, and may be basalt. But the real nature of the mantle, the part it plays in events within the planet, is still mostly guesswork. If the mantle could be studied directly by actually digging into it, certain big questions, such as those about mountain-building and continent-building, would be much easier to answer.

Unfortunately the outer boundary of the mantle, called the Mohorovicic Discontinuity (after A. Mohorovicic, the Croatian seismologist who first identified it), lies about 15 to 25 miles below the surfaces of the continents. Since the deepest drilling ever done by man, an oil well in Texas, is only a little over four miles deep, the possibilities of drilling to 15 miles or more look very slim indeed.

But oceanographers have found by seismic tests that the Discontinuity lies only a few miles below the bottoms of some of the deeper ocean trenches. If a drilling assembly can be successfully operated from a ship through several miles of water, perhaps the mantle can be reached. Drifting of the ship will have to be prevented, and steadiness will have to be maintained during bad weather. The task will not be easy.

Born out of volcanoes—*Oahu, like other Hawaiian Islands, was built miles high from Pacific bottom by lava outbursts during past million years. Islands are still being built up by occasional volcanic activity. Prominent mountain range here is Koolau.*

This so-called Mohole Project may answer many questions. Will a core of the mantle turn out to be of the same material as the crust? Will it be changed somewhat by heat and pressure—or completely different chemically? These matters are of intense interest to science.

The temperature at various levels in the mantle may offer clues as to whether there really are convectional currents inside the planet. Such currents could affect terrestrial magnetism, mountain building, the wandering of land masses, even the formation of continents.

Cores from the undersea crust may consist of material that has been little changed since the crust formed billions of years ago. Tests of radioactivity, if it exists in this material, may tell its age —that is, when the crust actually formed.

The 1,000 to 3,000 feet of undisturbed sediments on the ocean bottom may represent Earth's entire history since its birth. Fossils in the cores of sediments may indicate when life first appeared in the seas. Magnetic minerals will provide evidence as to the wandering of the poles and, perhaps, as to continental drift. Changes in sediments from layer to layer may give hints as to ocean currents and world climates in past ages.

Meteoritic material in the sediments will be of special interest to astronomers. Bits of rock and metal from outer space have been falling into the oceans since the planet was born; and these, accumulated in the sediments, may tell much about happenings in our solar system in its earliest days. Some scientists hope the Mohole will reveal whether Earth was once molten, forming a crust as it cooled, or was a sphere of cold matter which became larger and hotter as its gravitational force attracted more and more material from surrounding space.

One thing is sure: the cores from the Mohole, cores which will be just a few pounds of sediments or rock captured in a pipe, are likely to be some of the most interesting material ever studied by science. The first core brought up will mark a new era in oceanography.

Drilling Mohole—*Task will not be so easy as picture suggests. Distance to ocean bottom will be 3 to 5 miles; from there to mantle, 5 to 10 miles. Wind, waves, and currents will interfere with drilling.*

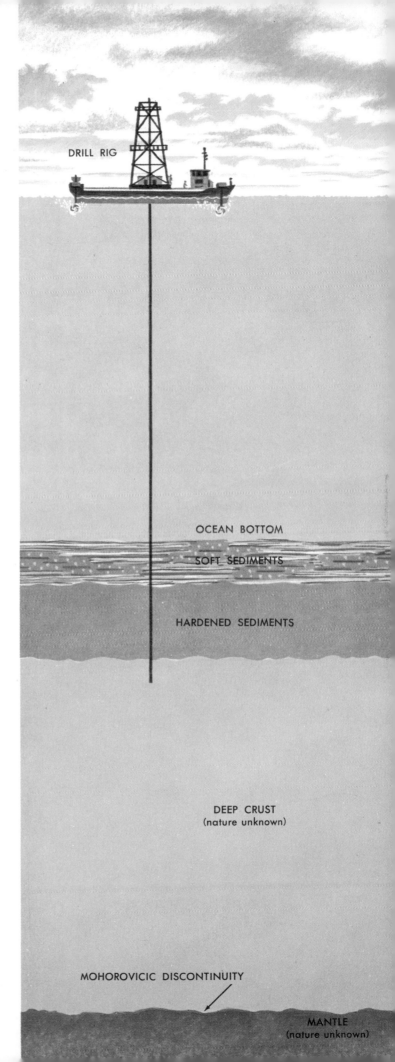

DRILL RIG

OCEAN BOTTOM

SOFT SEDIMENTS

HARDENED SEDIMENTS

DEEP CRUST
(nature unknown)

MOHOROVICIC DISCONTINUITY

MANTLE
(nature unknown)

Almost too strange to believe—*Children in museum, though accustomed to seeing dinosaur skeletons, still gaze in wonderment. Paleontologists themselves find it hard to grasp the enormous span of geologic time, the strangeness and the multitude of the living things that have roamed our Earth.*

Graveyards

THE CRUST of Earth is a vast graveyard. Here lie scattered the remains of living things that have roamed our planet or grown in its soils for two thousand million years. These fragments are entombed in the sedimentary rocks of mountains and sea bottoms, in the sands of deserts and beneath the grass of meadows. They are washed by the rains, frozen in ice, baked by the Sun, and blown through the air by the wind. We cannot pick up a handful of soil, anywhere in the world, without lifting with it some atoms of a being that once knew the Sun and the rain.

TRACES OF VANISHED LIFE

The traces of ancient living things, as found in the sedimentary rocks, are known as fossils. Most of them have lain in the rocks for millions of years, but gradually erosion has uncovered them. They appear in walls of canyons, the bedrocks of mountain slopes, along highways cut through hills, on rock floors of streams, in coal beds and in quarries. There is a good chance of seeing some in most places where there are sedimentary rocks.

Some of the ancient Greek philosophers suspected the true nature of fossils, but they never

Spirit writing?—*Fossils and odd mineral forms were once believed to have been created by underground spirits. Above drawings, from Kircher's* Mundus Subterraneous, *1664, were supposed to be true representations of specimens actually found.*

really knew. For centuries afterward, and through the Middle Ages, odd ideas about fossils prevailed. Typical was the notion, already described, that fossils are the writings or charms of underground spirits.

Leonardo da Vinci in the fifteenth century had guessed correctly as to the origin of the sedimentary rocks. He was aware also that fossils are the traces of ancient life. Yet even by the mid-1700's, educated people generally believed fossils to be the remains of plants and animals buried under the debris of Noah's Flood only a few thousand years before.

By 1750 a few naturalists such as Jean Guettard (the man who called attention to the extinct volcanoes in southern France) had noticed that the fossils in rocks are generally very different from life forms existing now. Also, personal observation was beginning to convince them that the sedimentary rocks in which fossils are found are much older than a few thousand years. Perhaps fossils were the remains of life from ages long, long before the time of Noah's Flood!

A CONNECTED STORY OF THE PAST

Soon after 1800, this line of thought was picked up and developed further by the prominent French naturalist Georges Cuvier. Accustomed to comparing the structures of animals and plants, he noticed that the fossils in any particular stratum of rock usually differ from fossils in the strata above and below. The past history of Earth, he suspected, has been divided into distinct stages or phases, with a different set of plants and animals existing during each stage.

Twenty million years old—*Fossil leaf of ancient gingko plant was found in shale near Grand Coulee Dam, Washington. Fossils rarely show original colors.*

This train of thinking was carried further yet by William Smith, in England. Where sedimentary rocks are exposed, Smith reasoned, the layer at the top must be the one that formed most recently. As one works downward, the strata become older and older. Thus the strata are stacked up in order of their age.

Furthermore, Smith decided, fossils are clues to to the relative ages of rocks. For example, if a certain kind of shellfish fossil is found in a rock stratum near London, and exactly the same type of fossil is found in a stratum a hundred miles away, these strata must be of about the same age.

Tramping over the hills and valleys of England, mapping the rock formations and checking the fossils, Smith prepared the way for another great English geologist, Sir Charles Lyell. It was Lyell who made geology a real science. Traveling all over Europe, he observed and thought about the evidence of Earth's history in many forms—the folded and faulted Alps, volcanoes old and new,

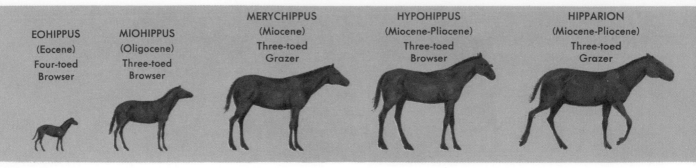

| EOHIPPUS (Eocene) Four-toed Browser | MIOHIPPUS (Oligocene) Three-toed Browser | MERYCHIPPUS (Miocene) Three-toed Grazer | HYPOHIPPUS (Miocene-Pliocene) Three-toed Browser | HIPPARION (Miocene-Pliocene) Three-toed Grazer |

Horses then and now—*Forms and relative sizes of these horses, beginning with primitive Eohippus at left, span 50 million years.*

changing sea levels, erosion, rock stratification, and the fossils which made it possible to see in all these things a connected story.

THE PARADE OF LIFE

The study of fossils, however, raised a hard question. Just *how* have the continual changes in the structures of living things occurred?

An answer was given in 1858 and the following years by the English naturalist Charles Darwin. New physical traits, said Darwin, keep appearing in living things from generation to generation. Those traits that help in the battle for existence tend to survive in a species, and those that are less useful tend to drop out. Thus the procession of life through the ages is a procession of changing forms. Over millions of years, the fish form leads to the amphibian, the amphibian to the reptile, and the reptile to the mammal.

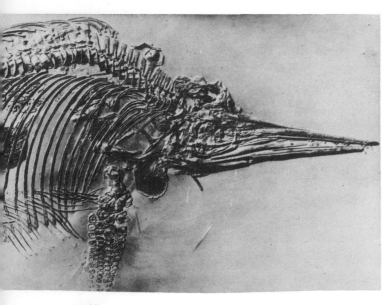

Like other naturalists of his time, Darwin half-believed that traits are developed by individuals according to need, and are then passed along to the offspring. Biologists have since learned that new traits are due to changes in the genes, or units of heredity that are passed along from generation to generation. Changes in genes are apparently random and have nothing to do with the needs of the individual in his environment.

Darwin's theory of natural selection did, however, start modern science on its way to an understanding of life of the past. Today, when we look at a fossil, we know it for what it is: not just a trace of a dead thing, an odd relic from yesterday, but a link in one of the long chains of life.

THE MAKING OF FOSSILS

In our imagination, let us travel backward 400 million years into the past.

On a sea bottom, a little animal called a trilobite—somewhat like our horseshoe crab—dies. Before its body can be eaten by another animal, an ocean current covers it with sand.

Hundreds of years pass. The slow trickling of water through the little animal's remains carries these away, bit by bit. The weight of sand above gradually closes the space. At last nothing is left of the trilobite but an imprint, buried deep in sand that is gradually turning to sandstone.

Millions of years go by. The old sea bottom rises, higher and higher, until at last it is a mountain range. Today, 400 million years after the

"Fish lizard"—*Bones of ichthyosaur, as well as imprints of other body parts, were preserved in detail. Fish-like reptile lived 160 million years ago.*

EQUUS
(Modern)
Single-toed Grazer

trilobite died, a stone image of it lies in the bedrock of the Canadian Rockies, 14,000 feet above the sea. . . .

Now let us go back 180 million years to the region that is now Connecticut. Swift rivers are eroding high mountains nearby, carrying red sands and clays into the lowlands. Walking on its hind legs along a muddy bank is an early dinosaur, *Anchisaurus*. This slender, speedy reptile, probably around seven or eight feet long, is leaving birdlike tracks.

The next day, a rain in the mountains causes the stream to flood over its banks a little—enough to fill some of the tracks with new sand.

Millions of years pass. The tracks become buried under hundreds of feet of sandstone and shale.

At last it is the twentieth century. Erosion in the Connecticut River valley has uncovered the ancient tracks. And—who knows?—these exposed tracks may be noticed by a geologist on a fossil hunt, or a family on a picnic.

Now we look back to 250 million years ago. The sea, creeping up from the ancient Gulf of Mexico, has covered part of the Mississippi Valley. Along its eastern shores are the swamps where coal measures are being laid. On its bottoms, beneath deeper water, limestones are forming.

Ages pass—a span 120,000 times as long as the whole Christian era. The sea bottom is now dry land. Man, a very busy newcomer on the planet, has opened quarries in the old limestones and is digging out thousands upon thousands of blocks for building stone. This is shipped all over the country for use in churches and other fine

Where a giant passed by—*Typical large, three-toed footprints in Montana streambed are dinosaur's. Prints were preserved by material which filled them.*

buildings. Some of it, if you look closely, is seen to be packed with shells—so packed with shells that you see almost nothing else.

A curious end for creatures that lived on sea bottoms of 250 million years ago!

ON THE TRAIL OF PREHISTORIC LIFE

The bodies of nearly all living things are destroyed and scattered soon after death. The chance that any particular animal or plant will be preserved as a fairly complete fossil may be only one in a million.

Even so, the fossils occurring in sedimentary rocks are enormous in number and variety. Old sea bottoms entombed not only trilobites and shellfish, but all sorts of seaweeds, true fishes, scorpions, worms and their burrows, sea reptiles, corals, and other forms of life by the billion, including types familiar today and those long since vanished from the planet. Strata formed by lakes and streams, and by wind-blown desert sands, provide fossils ranging from the earliest land plants to the first amphibians and birds, from

tree ferns to dinosaurs, from insects to mammals and all the rest.

Many fossils are simply imprints of bodies, skin, bones, or shells. Some contain hard parts of the original animals—that is, the actual bones and shells.

Some fossils, such as the ancient fallen logs in the Petrified Forest of Arizona, still show the original plant or animal structure. Water has filtered through the remains and gradually replaced them with minerals.

Many fossils are in the form of casts. Rock waste has filled in the hollow left by the decayed plant or animal. Still other fossils are seen as only a faint color pattern in the rock, recognizable by no one but the expert.

Some pieces of shale will split so as to reveal thin layers of black material inside. This is carbon, formed from decayed plants and animals.

In some sedimentary rocks there are few fossils or none at all. A sandstone formed in freshwater lakes before life existed outside the sea

Extracting a fossil—*Freeing perishable remains such as bone or skin from rock takes expert knowledge.*

170

would have no fossils of plants or animals, though it might show ripple marks made by waves on a beach. A limestone formed mainly by minerals precipitated by sea water may offer very few fossils. Fossils can be destroyed by water trickling between the rock grains, or by heat and pressure.

DETECTIVE WORK WITH FOSSILS

Most fossils are just bits and pieces. The few whole ones are often twisted, crumpled, and flattened. Making sense out of such remains is a job for experts.

Such experts are known as paleontologists. (The name comes from Greek words meaning "ancient," "things," and "study.") Paleontologists explore regions for fossils, dig the fossils out, treat them with preservatives, ship them back to the museums, piece the fragments together, examine them with microscopes, test them with chemicals, slice them into thin sheets to examine their inner structures, compare them with other fossils and with forms of life existing today, and check them against drawings and descriptions prepared by other experts.

When rock containing fossils is being removed from larger slabs, this must be done with great care. Measures must be taken to preserve those fossils, such as bones, which may start falling to pieces when exposed to air.

To an expert, even a tiny piece of fossil material—a bit of bone, a part of a leaf imprint—may be an important clue to the nature of the ancient plant or animal. From odds and ends of fossils, paleontologists can sometimes figure out what certain prehistoric forms of life looked like. But it is not true that an expert can take a single bone of an unknown animal and, with this alone to guide him, construct a skeleton like that of the original animal. The result might be—as every careful scientist knows—something quite fantastic!

UNVEILING FORMER WORLDS

Today, thanks to fossils and the labor of geologists, just about everyone has heard about trilobites, dinosaurs, pterodactyls, giant ferns—the whole parade of prehistoric life.

All our knowledge of this life of the past comes from fossils and the rocks in which they are found. The fossils in any stratum are clues to the kinds of plants and animals that were living in the region when the sediments were laid down. The particular characteristics of the rock itself—whether limestone, shale, or sandstone—indicates whether the sediments were laid down on a sea floor, in a swamp, in a desert, or in a riverbed. By putting together all the clues, the scientist builds up his picture of ancient worlds.

In certain shale formations in Wyoming, the bones of the clumsy, 65-foot dinosaur *Brontosaurus* have been found. In other strata of about the same age are remains of such animals as dragonflies, cockroaches, fishes, and the winged reptiles known as pterosaurs. The abundant plant remains include rushes and tree ferns—types which flourish in swamps. Thus the geologist, detail by detail, builds up a picture of *Brontosaurus,* his animal neighbors, and the swamps where they all lived long ago.

Now the geologist assumes, as William Smith did, that the stratum he is studying is probably younger than any stratum below it, and older than any above it. This means that the order of strata indicates the order in which ancient life appeared. In a single cliff, then, there might be the record of millions of years. Following the strata from bottom to top, the geologist may find evidence of how the animals, plants, and their

Putting carnivorous dinosaur together—*Fossil skeletons may be jumbled when discovered, with bones of different animals mixed in. Sorting and reconstruction are job for highly trained scientists.*

environments in this region *changed* during the ages of history represented by the strata. Thus, in the Wyoming shale, he may see how the swamp where *Brontosaurus* lived dried up, the climate became cooler, and new types of animals and plants replaced the old ones.

FOSSILS: A KEY TO AGE

Reconstructing the past by following rock strata is often, however, extremely difficult. No region contains a complete record in the rocks. From most regions the strata have been removed partly or wholly by erosion. In mountain areas they have been cracked, tilted, bent, sunk, raised, pushed out of line, and even jumbled. Some formations lie so deep that their nature is unknown; many have been covered with deep soils and lavas. Every region that does have sedimentary

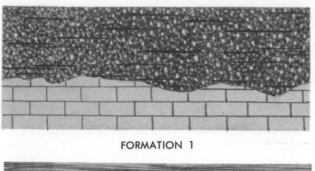

FORMATION 1

FORMATION 2

Break in the story—*In both formations here, upper stratum was laid down after top of lower one eroded away. First, limestone was laid down under water; then region rose to become land, and erosion occurred. Finally, eroded limestone was covered by new sediments. Dividing line between old and new represents gap in history of region. Such lines of division are known as unconformities.*

rocks has them in different amounts and different combinations. Wherever the geologist starts "reading" a formation, he faces a new problem.

The key to that problem, as William Smith showed, is the geologist's knowledge of fossils. In any stratum containing fossils the geologist will probably find some that he recognizes, and these will be clues as to which period of Earth history the stratum represents.

Suppose that sandstone in a Wisconsin hill is found to contain the same kinds of trilobites that are found in a certain sandstone stratum of the Canadian Rockies. The two sandstones, it can be assumed, were laid down during about the same period of Earth history. This will be so even if the strata just above and just below the Wisconsin sandstone yield fossils different from those found in the strata just above and just below the Canadian stratum.

Fossils are the key to the relative ages of sedimentary strata all over the world.

Once the period of a stratum has been determined, that stratum may indicate the relative age of rocks next to it. Suppose a geologist finds an old lava flow covered partly by sedimentary strata, and sees signs that the upper strata formed

over the lava after this cooled. He may then assume that the lava is older than the strata over it, and younger than the strata beneath it. This lava flow, in turn, may then indicate the relative ages of sedimentary rocks that touch it elsewhere.

Thus the geologist works through a region, checking the order of the bedrocks and the fossils in them. Gradually he fills out the chronology for that region during a part, or parts, of its total history. As he becomes acquainted with more and more regions, he finds that the history of each one helps to fill gaps in the histories of the others. Finally, the geological past of whole continents begins to take shape.

The story of Earth is told on countless pages that are scattered all over the globe. The pages

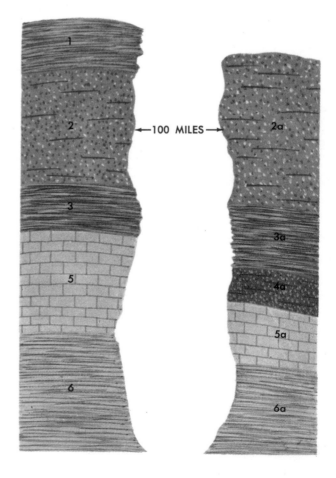

Rock puzzle—*Opposite rock exposures present typical problem. Were they once part of same layers stretching across 100 miles? If so, were missing strata (1a and 4) eroded away or never laid down? Or are the exposures unrelated?*

172

are not numbered, there are many duplicates, many are torn and tattered, and some are missing. It is the geologist's task—and his joy—to put them in the right order and read them through.

HOW LONG AGO?

Ordinarily, the geologist is more concerned about the relative ages of strata than about their absolute ages. He needs to know not whether a certain stratum is fifty or seventy-five million years old, but just where it fits into Earth history.

Naturally, he would like to know exactly how many years the layer took to form, and how long ago this happened. But in most cases this information is hard to determine. Sediments pile up at different speeds in different places, and even in the same place the speed changes. Rates of erosion, changes in animal and plant forms, schedules of volcanic activity—these offer few clues to calendar dates.

Sometimes the age of the formation can be determined by means of the "atomic clock." This is not an actual clock, but a method by which an expert can tell the approximate age of certain radioactive minerals found here and there in the igneous rocks. The age of the mineral may indicate the age of the rock containing it.

Bits of uraninite, for instance, occur in certain igneous rocks. Uraninite contains the radioactive element uranium. The atoms of the uranium are unstable; particles of which they are made are gradually escaping; and so the original uranium atoms gradually break down into atoms of lead—a lighter, stable element. Now, the rate at which uranium atoms change into lead atoms is known: therefore, after measuring the proportion of lead that has formed in the uraninite, the geologist can calculate the number of years ago the uraninite formed. This number is probably the age of the rock in which the uraninite occurs, because the uranium started becoming lead at the moment when the uraninite formed in the cooling magma.

According to this test, the oldest igneous rocks in North America are in Manitoba, Canada. Uraninite in these is about 2,400 million years old. But these rocks formed from magma that worked up through already existing metamor-

phosed strata—strata that formed probably before any life existed on this planet. What the ages of these older rocks may be we can only guess.

Still older than the igneous rocks in Manitoba are some formations near Salisbury, Southern Rhodesia, in Africa. Uraninite testing here indicates an age of 2,700 million years.

TELL-TALE CARBON

The breakdown of uranium is so slow that it makes a poor yardstick for periods of mere thousands of years. The isotope carbon-14, which breaks down much faster, is better for these shorter periods.

Fossils as keys to age—*Opposite exposures here look alike. But are they? Trilobites found in strata 4 and 4a are of Lower Cambrian (see chart, page 174). Fossils in 3 and 3a are of Middle Cambrian, but the one in 2a is Silurian—much later. Likewise, trilobite in 1a, typical of Devonian, is much younger than specimen in stratum 1, which is characteristically Ordovician. Geologist decides there was long break in rock story between strata 3a and 2a. The presence the unconformity (an erosion surface) between 3a and 2a is supporting evidence.*

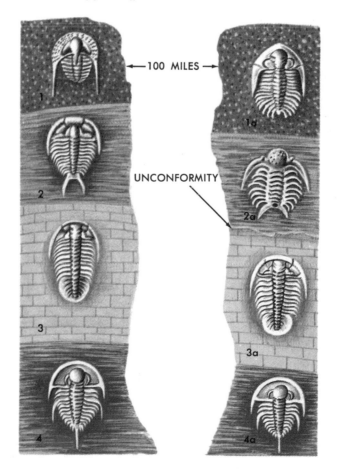

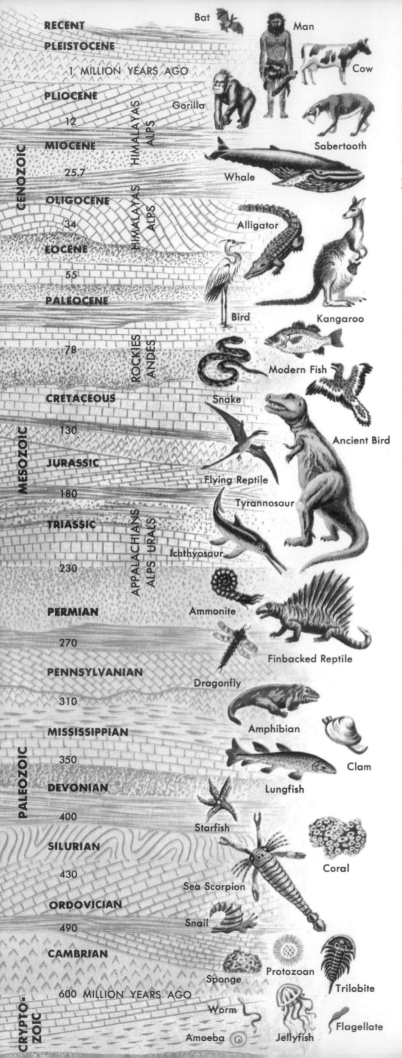

Carbon-14 is absorbed from the atmosphere by tissues of plants and animals during life, but not after death. Therefore the stage of breakdown of the carbon-14 in any dead tissue indicates how long ago death occurred. The test is accurate to within about 1,000 years for periods up to 35,000 years.

In Wisconsin, for example, the carbon-14 test was made on fossil trees that were felled and buried by advancing ice in the recent glacial period. The test gave 11,000 to 12,000 years as the time that has elapsed since the trees died. Certain other geological evidence shows that in this area the ice sheet *was* advancing just about 11,000 to 12,000 years ago.

The age of plant and animal remains may point to still further information. Just as in Wisconsin the tree remains dated the ice sheet, so in another place fish remains may date an ancient lake, bones may tell the age of a rock stratum, and trees buried under desert sands may tell how long ago a region was fertile.

THE GEOLOGICAL COLUMN

A century and a half of geology has given us a remarkably detailed, though still incomplete, record of Earth's past billion years. The first three to four billion years are still wrapped in mystery. There are only the faintest clues to suggest how the planet was born, and how the lands and oceans came into being. But about two billion years ago, geologists believe, the continents and seas reached something like their present form, and very likely some simple organisms appeared in the oceans. Events since then have been a series of geological changes rather like those we see around us today.

Earth history seems naturally divided into eras. Boundaries between them are not always clear, but each era had its sets of typical animals and plants. Each ended with important geological events, such as outbursts of volcanic activity, changes in climate, the building of mountain

Geological column—*Periods of Earth history are shown in order, from oldest (at bottom) to most recent. Uplift has occurred in mountains during periods indicated. Spans of time are estimates, revised occasionally, but order of events is well established.*

ranges, and the rising and sinking of lands. These events changed the conditions of life, so that some old animal and plant forms died out and new ones appeared.

The eras, in turn, divide into periods. These shorter time spans were separated, like the eras, by important geological events. The list of eras and periods, and of the major events and changing forms of life, is known as the Geological Column.

ALMOST TOO STRANGE TO BELIEVE

The Geological Column gives us a bird's eye view of the planet's history, yet it can hardly begin to suggest the enormous span of geologic time, the multitudes of living things that have come and gone, and the ancient scenes that are no more. Behind the name of each single period is a history too vast for the mind to comprehend, and sometimes almost too strange to believe.

What are the meanings of these odd names—Cambrian and Devonian, Pennsylvanian and Jurassic, Eocene and Pleistocene?

They mean sea bottoms heaving up to become Rockies, Alps, Himalayas . . . Ice sheets over the Mississippi Valley, northern France and Germany, and the Congo . . . Rivers unendingly heaping up the rock waste to depths of miles . . . The roots of submarine mountains, the dark ocean trenches, preparing their earthquakes . . . Greenland and Antarctica, places of Sun and waving palms . . . Wyoming, a place of swamps and dinosaurs . . . The slow, irresistible transformation of matter in the hearts of mountains . . . And, everywhere on the planet, the forms of life multiplying and struggling and finding the new forms that have led to man and his neighbors of the twentieth century—a century which is a fraction of a second on the geological clock, whose hands still point to a morning hour.

The living past—*Natural scenery everywhere, like a bridge across time, links us with Earth's long past. This picturesque ruin is Owachomo Bridge, Arches National Monument, Utah.*

INDEX

(**Boldface** indicates pages on which subjects are illustrated)

177